44 Things

KIRSTY GUNN is the author of five previous novels: *The Boy and the Sea*, *Featherstone*, *Rain*, *The Keepsake* and *This Place You Return to Is Home*. She lives with her family in London and Scotland.

Also by Kirsty Gunn

KIRSTY GUNN

44 Things

A Year of Life at Home

Atlantic Books
LONDON

First published in Great Britain in 2006
by Atlantic Books, an imprint of Grove
Atlantic Ltd.

Copyright © Kirsty Gunn 2006

The moral right of Kirsty Gunn to be
identified as the author of this work has
been asserted in accordance with the
Copyright, Designs and Patents Act of
1988.

The author would like to acknowledge
the following, from which extracts have
appeared in this book: Raymond Carver,
Where I'm Calling From (Harvill, 1993); Carol
Shields, *Unless* (Fourth Estate, 2002);
Alice Munro, *Runaway* (Chatto & Windus,
2005); Jayne Anne Phillips, *Motherkind*
(Alfred A Knopf, 2000); Tessa Hadley,
Accidents in the Home (Jonathan Cape,
2002); Helen Simpson, *Hey, Yeah Right Get
a Life* (Jonathan Cape, 2001); J.M.
Barrie, *Peter Pan* (Penguin, 2005);
C.S. Lewis, *The Lion, the Witch and the Wardrobe*
(Geoffrey Bles/HarperCollins, 1950);
E.B. White, *Charlotte's Web* (HarperCollins,
1952); Rumer Godden, *Miss Happiness and
Miss Flower* (Macmillan, 1961); Justin
Tussing, *The Best People in the World* (Fourth
Estate, 2006); Yann Martel, *Life of Pi*
(Canongate, 2002); Virginia Woolf,
The Waves (The Hogarth Press, 1943);
Katherine Mansfield, *At the Bay*
(Weidenfeld & Nicolson,1996).

Every effort has been made to trace
or contact all copyright-holders. The
publishers will be pleased to make good
any omissions or rectify any mistakes
brought to their attention at the earliest
opportunity.

2 3 4 5 6 7 8 9

A CIP catalogue record for this book is
available from the British Library.

ISBN 978 1 84354 552 1

Design by Lindsay Nash
Printed in Germany by Bercker

Atlantic Books
An imprint of Grove Atlantic Ltd
Ormond House
26–27 Boswell Street
London WC1N 3JZ

For all our families

Contents

CONTENTS

CONTENTS

On the Contents of this Book

44 Things is a response to the life that goes on around me as I live and work with my family at home. It is not a journal or a diary; it is not a memoir, but, rather, a kind of scrapbook, a place where I can put together the various pieces of writing that have come about as a direct result of events and pieces of news and information that arrive into my domestic world on a daily basis.

None of these are grand-scale dispatches. A friend may call or write a letter; I reply in what looks a little like a poem. I watch my children and scribble something on the back of an envelope. I read a review and it reminds me of an essay I'd like to write. There's a short story about a funeral that jiggles about in my head as I do the dishes...

And so on...

Forty-four pieces of different kinds of writing that have one thing in common — they are written by this woman, me, who lives at this time in her life fully and imaginatively sustained by what goes on in her domestic world. A world that is as rich and interesting and inspiring as any other I may choose to live in. And though *44 Things* is not made in the way of other books — to seem as though formed in one continuous piece, like a length of cloth emerging from the loom — it is instead something come together piece by piece, in bits, sections, squares of text that may be joined one bit to the next, and has unity, I think. These parts do make up a whole. It is written in the way it is because life at home is the way it is: chaotic, undecided, fragmentary. How could I ever be grandiose in scale, in intention, when the draft of a short story is fiddled with next to a plate of uneaten Weetabix?

So yes, it's a different kind of literary life, this life of 'things', it comes about in a different way. Here at home there's nothing like the time for that concentrated, ruminative sort of work that takes place in the study or library... But how interesting it is, nevertheless, to find a new way of finding words.

Everything here appears pretty much in the order in which it was written. At the end of the book I've put together notes that describe how each piece came about, or give some extra information that sets it in context. The entries are listed one to forty-four on the back pages. And as to why there are forty-four entries in all? You'll find out in a minute when you turn the page and read the first 'thing'…

44 Things

1

An Introduction

On the night of my forty-fourth birthday we went, my husband and I, with our two little girls, to the Brasserie at Brompton Cross. I'd requested this as my birthday present. David and I had started out with all kinds of rather grand plans — from a really fancy dinner out, just the two of us, getting the babysitter in, right through to talking about a party maybe, some kind of groovy little event with dancing, or a weekend away, to Paris or Rome or somewhere with a beautiful hotel (my birthday fell on a Saturday this year) — but no, in the end I decided that what I wanted most was a whole day in bed reading and then getting up and going out with my own family, my husband and daughters, to an early supper.

I've always had a clean, well-lighted place in my heart for the Brasserie. It has nothing but the sweetest, simplest memories attached to it, times that remind me of all the adult phases of my life. There is my sister and me and her lovely first husband in green face powder and full evening dress in our crazy eighties youth... There is that New Year's Eve hung-over brunch with my oldest friend in the world, when we ordered rosé instead of coffee. I can see myself at breakfast, lunch, supper... Falling in love with my husband, registering the birth of our first daughter... It's the place where I go when I need to confirm that the world is a marvellous, unchanging home, safe and jolly, where the maître d' is the same, with his beautiful, round, smiling Belgian face that gets older and nicer with the years, and where the waiters with their long white aprons and dark suits are the same, doing the same things, in the same order. It's not fancy, the Brasserie, it's not a swishly expensive place. I order the same dishes every time — Roquefort salad, minute steak, spinach, crème caramel — and the bill, like everything else, never seems to change either. The most recent time I was there was with a painter friend, also a mother, and we talked about our work and the clothes our daughters chose to wear. We were too early for supper, really, but way too late for lunch; we were pretty much alone in the room. But our napkins were 'shook' out for us, as my daughter Katherine and the poet Gerard Manley Hopkins (in his poem 'The world is charged with the grandeur of God. It shall fall out like shining from shook foil...') like to say, and it was, as ever, a perfect little time.

But this night, the night of my forty-fourth birthday, something else took place in my heart that added to, made all the more glittery and just like shook foil, all the times I'd ever sat at the table there. It was an awareness, in the keenest sense, of the feeling of my life. As I said, I have always thought of the Brasserie as a formal kind of backdrop to certain life moments — markers, if you like. I am a writer, after all, and these kinds of things can become stories; of course, I would be self-aware that way. But this evening something was sensed that was more than that. Something more personal again.

The two little girls were wearing their Swiss-muslin white dresses, trimmed in lemon velvet with puff sleeves and under-skirts — what I call their 'Natasha *War and Peace* Dresses' — and they

3

were excited, having a wonderful time. They wriggled on their banquette, ate fries, came with me dancing to choose a special pudding from the trolley. My husband and I drank champagne, talked… And all the time I was thinking: *This*. It was the feeling of being consumed completely by the moment. Being in the centre of my own time. Knowing that all the while I was loitering about upon this old world, knocking about from room to room, I had this moment now, with my husband and daughters, our faces reflected in the mirrors and before us the glasses, the bread, the white cloth. Like a bead, the present, the awareness of it. Like a bead on a string I might have pressed into my palm as I slid off towards death… *This*.

'When are you going to get back into your writing fully?' asked my husband then. We'd been having some part of a conversation about publishing, writing, people we knew who were bringing out books, how they were doing. 'The novel,' David said. 'Your new novel. When do you think you'll get started properly with that?' I looked at him; he took a sip of his wine. And from out of the utterly transfixing sense of the present that I was experiencing, with him, our daughters, as I listened to our talk, out of everything, cutting up minute steak, cooling off pommes frites for the girls, feeding spinach into their mouths, came the spontaneous reply which went something like, 'You know, I don't think I can even begin to think that way right now.'

It's true. I couldn't. I can't. My daughters were at that time six and three; at the time of writing they still are, and suddenly it had occurred to me, came straight out of the present to settle in me like those two little girls' bodies so often settled in me... The weight of the time of mothering. Six years. I had Millie the day my collection of short stories came out in the UK, Katherine two and a half years later, just before the publication of my third novel (I remember going through the galley proofs while washing all the tiny baby sleepsuits that her sister had worn in preparation for her arrival). And all that time in those intervening years I thought I had pulled it off: writing books, having babies. Yet here I was six years down the line and my output had diminished, my activities as a writer — to be present, active, as my agent puts it, 'out there' — these had been curtailed, made secondary to my activities as a wife and mother.

This is exactly what I wanted, too. For myself. For our daughters. Before I became pregnant I remember saying to my husband that if a Faustian pact should present itself to me I would be a mother rather than a writer — a mother always, always first, and I hold to that acknowledgement always. This is what you wanted, I say to myself, this is what you got. Never, ever, would I become one of those who made a virtue, profession even, of complaint. I chose, like so many of us who are educated and older and who know what we want and make informed decisions choose, mothering. That's a contract we made; it's fixed. As I see it, you don't turn around after making that choice and say you don't want it like that after all. You don't break a promise that way, step in to try and close down something that began like a prayer, an act of faith, because you've changed your mind.

So there I was, replying to my husband's question. 'You know, I don't think I can even begin to think that way.' And there were the girls in their white dresses. And I was far, far from even starting to write this big novel for which the Scottish Arts Council had so generously awarded me their thoughtful and important Writer's Bursary, and in which my publishers and agent, despite my relative inactivity, maintained active interest. For what was going on here? Getting back to the novel? What was it about, this question of my writing, what I was doing with my time? All I can say is rather along the same lines as the words my older daughter, Millie, comes out with in her response to her younger sister's grandiloquence when she attempts it. 'Oh blah, blah, blah yourself, Kaaaafffrin!' she says. For, really, what... novel? What had happened, rather, in those intervening years when I thought I was cleverly managing the motherhood and authorship combination, was that motherhood, actually, had claimed me in the end.

But hang on a moment here. 'Claimed'? I wanted to be claimed! And who was it prescribed I could only be one or the other, anyway? Lots of women wrote books while they looked after their children... didn't they? I could get a nanny, like they did, to help. I could be like Toni Morrison and have a job and have babies and still write *Beloved*. I could follow the model of so many writers I admire and manage, with all kinds of clever juggling, to do... both. That's, after all, what I'd always thought I was going to do. Both. And to a certain extent, I had. But. What

I recognized suddenly that night when I replied to David's question was that motherhood *had changed the way I thought about writing*. It hadn't necessarily changed what I wanted to write about – I have always written about families, that most intimate life, and about children with, as Frank O'Connor puts it, their frank, calm gaze of 'hysterical clarity' – but it had changed the way I went about setting it down. Gone, in short, was the grand act. Gone was the concept of the desk, the routines, the six set hours of a day. Gone were the long uninterrupted periods of thinking and reading around the writing, planning themes, researching... Gone, gone, gone the closed study door. The words were being formed in a different way.

At the time of writing this my desk is situated on a landing at the top of the stairs. I hear everything: the clattering, the quiet, the doorbell, the calls for help, 'Mum!' 'Mummy!' 'I need you!' I'm on a landing, on the stairs, between flights. And it feels, it is, absolutely right. 'I don't think I can even begin to think that way right now,' I said to my husband about starting on a novel – because how can I begin to work in that way from the stairs? Make a novel, I mean. Embark on something that requires that kind of scale around it. I can't begin to compete with other writers in that, by which I mean write alongside those who still maintain about them the surety of the closed study door. I want to hear the 'Mum!' 'Neither,' I said to my husband, 'do I think I necessarily want to be "out there". Start writing the big reviews, go to all the parties. Really, I want to… be here.' By now the girls had left the table and were sort of running around the restaurant; they were talking to people, performing slightly, doing little kinds of shows. They were being either charming or deeply annoying — my eye was on them but I couldn't be completely sure. 'All I think I can do,' I said to David, 'is find a different way of writing, make a different kind of writing that's on another scale. That's of another genre altogether, somehow. A genre that at this moment doesn't even exist. Like I can make some… things,' I said. 'That's it. That's what I'll do. I'll make some… things.'

This, by the way, is not to be deliberately or coyly annoyingly belittling of my work or the plan I had for it. I've always been intensely self-aware around the business of naming my writing. I've always loathed, actually, the moniker of 'novel' with its current associations of entertainment and endless narrative drive and fulfilment. I've never thought of myself as being anything like a poet, even though I'm interested in that kind of allusive, technique-inclined approach to writing; there are too many notions of literariness and grandeur attached there that would make me feel shy and self-conscious. My short stories are not so much stories as writing about things that happen, or don't really happen much... So when I talk about 'things', as I do when I introduce my work, in interview or at readings, I am being as truthful as I can be about the way I think of my different pieces of writing.

The kind of 'things' I was proposing now, however, though of the same stock as that other work, were to be different, too. I was thinking about a different way of writing, on a different scale, remember. I wasn't moving towards the idea of completion as in the past with a book of stories or a novel. What I was thinking towards, rather, was something that fitted appropriately and honestly against the shape of my life. It was to be about the way I'm living now as a wife and mother, as a kind of domestic response to that life. A writing less fixed, more organic than the notion of completed, published work, the kind of writing that would come not from behind a closed study door but out of a desk on the stairs in the middle of a house. And it would be no less important for that, for being made on the stairs while I heard the cry 'I need you!', no less imaginative or open or true than any of those other, more formal, published works of mine.

So, 'I'm going to make some things this year' is what I said to my husband. We're moving into a new home, I have to sort that out. We have these two little Walsungs (our Wagnerian nick-names for the girls). There are the pets (two cats and a dog). I have my friends... I'm not going to go off somewhere now and write some novel. I want to attend to these other matters – of care and responsibility, home-making, mothering... I want to do that now, while it's all here around me. 'Time enough,' I said, 'when no one will cry out for me in the middle of the night or want me to come rushing because they've trodden on a pin. One day I won't be standing in a park pushing a swing, showing someone who's six how to make a big long "t" or put glue on a piece of paper so that another piece of paper will stick to it... Time enough then to write my big novel, when my help is no longer needed. When I'm no longer required to sit on Millie's bed and hear her bang on about death and how old you can be to be an angel, when it's no longer necessary to watch and be admiring while Katherine proudly and carefully puts on her own shoes. Which isn't to say that other writers don't do this and write amazing books too – not to say they don't do it all the time. But I don't feel I have the will,' I said to David, 'the ability, actually, to do both. Being this mother that I have become for our two daughters has taken me up, and any novels I might write now are in their words, the story in their lives. For now, for me, the grand literary idea is gathered up completely in the idea of a child of mine startling from a dream in the depths of the night. I can do no more, right now, than attend to the sound of that waking.

'In fact,' I said to my husband, 'here I am, I'm forty-four' – we raised our glasses – 'so I'll make forty-four things. That's all I'll do. It won't be earth-shattering, it'll just be me making writing from and for my life, about the way my life is now. There'll be pieces on motherhood, the children, responses to letters and calls from friends. There'll be some short stories,

I think, and fragments from longer fictions. There might be essays, notes about motherhood, families. I'm going to make the work as it arises directly from my concerns, out of the texture and priorities of my life at home — it's a good life, an interesting life and deserves to be written about; I do believe in it. And I don't think I'm alone in this,' I said. 'A lot of people, I bet, a lot of mothers, parents, will understand about working and thinking this way. Forty-four things,' I said again and I felt — it feels — absolutely right.

At that point there was a crash and a cry from under the table. I ducked below to see what was going on.

2

Wahine

You went out to that rock,
Emma said,
and let go somewhere there into
the green midwinter sea
and blowy air
the contents of the little bag
that Evelyn had made and all of silk,
your fine, fine dust,
your boy...

You did, his mother, you,
his rock and boat and sea, the one
who carried, bore and

held him, *Jesus*, there inside you
rocking on your tides and waves,
growing cell by cell, you had him
in you all entire and yet
you made it out there
in the cold and
opened up
and let
him
go…

And it makes me think, you know, remember,
just as Emma said,
about the day that other boat
cracked open and let go her charge,
went down with it into the deep, and
you went out to that same rock and
went around it, yes, okay, but still
the wind bore down, the sea
ran dark and you and only you (the

rest of us can never know)
did feel within you how it was,
the split, the
break, the giving up
of all you'd carried, you,
wahine, woman, crafted
just the same to carry, carefully
to hold your cargo, keep it safe
upon this cold midwinter sea,
to hold and ever keep on holding
even while you let him go
to hold him, little boy, your son, always
to hold.

Wahine: Maori word for woman, also name of a passenger
ship that sank off the shores of Wellington, New Zealand,
in 1968.

3

Notes to Myself

I am a woman who writes and reads, who was educated to compete and be successful — academically, financially and politically — in the world. And I am also a woman who has chosen to have children and look after those children — not pass them on to a full-time nanny or institution but be the one who's elected herself to open up the homework bag, arrange for the little friends to come to tea. To kiss the bruised knee at the moment when the knee is bruised — this has been my choice.

The world for which I was educated, therefore, at this time of my life, I can no longer say is my world.

'You ask me if I'm lonely,' wrote Adrienne Rich in that beautiful collection of poems of hers, *Diving into the Wreck*, 'well, yes, then, lonely...', and for sure this choice of mine has put me somewhere else that's far away from the competitive bustle of profession and career, where men and women compete for advantage... I am not present there. I have made the active choice to 'disappear', if you like, in this way. I no longer make money as I used to, have power that way. 'You ask me if I'm lonely, well, yes, then, lonely...' The fact is, as the images of Rich's poem describe — a radar in the dark, a rowboat stilled upon frozen sands — the life I've chosen has taken me to a different place, and, just as her poem finishes with the idea of a self as a boat pulled up on a midwinter beach, 'made of neither ice nor mud but wood, with a gift for burning...', I see now that I, too, have been consumed by my bearing, my giving birth to, nursing and caring for my two children. To hold them, for as long as I can, always to hold them: this has been my choice. To feel myself break with tiredness at their needs and still want to crawl into bed beside them and feel my own breath at the soft base of their necks... This my desire, my burn.

I never expected it. I never thought I wanted it, this consummate need of children that devours me, sends me rigid with boredom and rage, sometimes, flattening me with a sense of failure and despair like no other, and also lifts me up like on wings with the euphoria of soaring, wondering happiness and love. Yet how I feel the reality of those contradictions and the life that contains them — so real, in fact, it's sometimes hard to find realities elsewhere. I can't remember certain things like I used to remember. Did I write that cheque for the gas last week? What kind of mortgage do we have? I don't seem interested any more in hanging onto facts like these. Neither do I express myself with the certainty I had before; I don't even think I have any certainties any more. Instead, I live in a somewhere else that's alive with questions and with questioning, and answers that lead only on to other, different answers. It's somewhere far away from those old certainties, this place, where sentences begun may end unfinished, and paragraphs dissolve away. A somewhere else where sometimes I can barely speak at all.

And what a place it is, too, that place where talking stops. As though the self's been stilled, shock-stilled sometimes, by all the busy, wondering neediness of a child. It can feel like there's nothing of you left. And yet there is. A different kind of sense that's born from all the chaos and the quiet... A different mind.

Is it like this for everyone as we get older? As we become parents and see our children grow? I don't know. All I do know is that I myself am burned through by my daughters' flames and I don't see now how I could walk out of the conflagration and pretend the fire never happened. I wouldn't want to pretend.

Yet it seems pretending is what we who are so burned are supposed to do. As someone I'll call Will A. put it recently, so gently and cleverly, as we were sitting next to each other at a publishing dinner talking of these things, 'You women,' he said, 'you mothers, when you come here, like tonight, when you enter the world to come to one of our meetings, or to a lunch, whatever... You look wonderful, you talk, you've done your hair, you've got shoes on... And all I can think is: you've just left your house behind you with your children in it and that must be like you've left somewhere... that's like a war zone, somewhere I can't even imagine...' And this is it entirely. For the world of home, of children, the world I've chosen, is this kind of other fenced-off land, a zone. When you're in it, it surrounds you. And as you walk away you hear its crashes and cries and tumbling down of walls – 'Mummy! Come here!' – long after you've turned the corner of your street. It seems you've made it out of the fire and it's like a miracle, a trick of the eye — well, maybe for some it's real, the pulling together of the old self out of the wreckage, but for me, no. To pretend I'm not affected by the place where I've just been would be on a level akin to pretending I'm good at sports. I can't do it. I may be tying back my hair as I go to the car, looking for change in a nice little bag for the bus, but in my head I'm still back there amongst the wild grab of legs and arms around my legs, the spilt food, the tears, the 'I'm so over you, Mum's, complaints, fights, desperate kisses. It takes me a while, really, to try and disentangle.

I wonder now if I ever will. For something occurred with the bringing of my daughters into the world and it fixed for me the night of my forty-fourth birthday. I don't want to pretend, act like it's easy to do this, have at once the professional public world and the other intensely private at-home one. As I said that night of my birthday, I don't want to 'complete a novel', get 'back to the big book'. I don't want to be part of something on that scale right now that would require me to function in ways that were in accordance with the expectations that that choice would bring. Instead, I want to respond to the world as it has become for me – a smaller world, perhaps, domestic, day to day, but vivid to my mind with possibilities and with chance, with changes and new ways of seeing, passion of a wild and delicate kind...

This is my world.

A friend writes to me about being a mother and she, like me, has no mother. My husband weeps, quickly and quietly at the nursery school door when dropping off our youngest daughter. Another friend tells me about the work she's trying to make, images of women, and how that whole notion of femininity has been shaken, changed by motherhood. My agent talks about playing *CBeebies* for his small son while working at his office and planning Bonfire Night. Another friend is seriously ill and is resting at home. It's in the midst of this that I write now. Short stories, sometimes, little pieces, essays, amazed actually that I get anything finished at all. I return again and again for strength and inspiration to the closed domestic universes created by Katherine Mansfield and Virginia Woolf – for the whole lives, lives within lives, that are succoured in their pages. I gather up the letters of my friends, artwork of my children. I read, I review a little. I talk about books and publishing with my husband, make lists for my day each day: Millie, 50p for a school project; Katherine, farm outing on the 28th. Bring seeds and twigs and cereal cartons to school on Monday; all water bottles to be named, please... I tick things off, I take care of the house, my children, my husband. I don't write novels. I'm making instead some things, like all of our mothers found time to make things; for me, pieces of writing that will mark this time in my life, that will show me my world.

I saw my face reflected in the mirror that night of my birthday and saw a woman who, as she sorted out the French fries and was not a lead columnist for the *LRB*, as she wiped spinach off a shoe and did not make a viable income, had everything she wanted. Though in the world for which she'd been educated, this woman was nowhere, was invisible, almost, not even close to approaching the doorway through which she could re-enter the place she'd left. 'You ask me if I'm lonely...' Still, she has everything.

Everything.

4

Small Pieces for the Girls

Haiku 1
(KATHERINE)

With eyes stinging in
the cold and setting sun, I
kneel and hold my child.

Small Poem
(MILLIE AND KATHERINE)

In our bath last night
I had in one arm
a fruit, and in the
other a flower.

These were my daughters.

Everything,
for one long second,
I could ever hope for,
or need.

Haiku 2
(KATHERINE)

Your naked back curved
like a pastry while you sat,
watched your sister draw.

Haiku 3
(MILLIE)

I hold your paper-clip
shoulder between my thumb
and finger, my love.

5

Domesticity in Literature:
The Art of the Ordinary

If art is the mirror we hold up to the world, then what grandeur is reflected there. Our cultural tradition shimmers and gleams with kings and queens, palaces and estates... From the plays of Aeschylus through Shakespeare and on, the idea persists that to warrant our attention events must occur on a grand scale. This is true of the history of painting and poetry as well as theatre, but in these spheres it has dissolved into more familiar contexts: soap opera, kitchen-sink drama, the fine art of real life as exemplified in Tracey Emin's *My Bed*... Art's mirror reflects all kinds of lives these days. Yet in our literature, grandiosity continues to preen itself before the glass. There may be fewer noblemen and landowners around than were present in our eighteenth- and nineteenth-century fictions, but the characters we meet on the page must still be important in the sense that they must do interesting things, have interesting things happen to them. They must be... *grand*, in the sense of being on a certain scale, psychologically if not socially. They must entertain us that way.

Where is the equivalent of a Chardin plate of ham or a James Kelman short story about missing the bus in our novels? Why has painting been able to shift its focus from the ermine trim of the queen's robe to the plate of fish and lemons on the rough wooden table, while literature remains in thrall to the fur?

In a recent article for the *Guardian*, A. S. Byatt, in reviewing a show of paintings at the National Gallery, 'The Stuff of Life', addressed the themes of the 'ordinary' in still life and portraiture, in those representations of homes and the things we keep there to give us meaning, security, responsibility. The paintings manipulate these things symbolically, for sure, but Byatt also argues for their value, firstly as beautifully made renditions of objects that are pleasing to us, a 'painting that understands and reproduces vision' that way, and secondly — and for me importantly — in the way the images celebrate, put forward for our attention, moments in ordinary life that we might otherwise miss. 'In the Velázquez,' she writes, 'an angry cook, wielding a pestle, glares out at us with the rage of all women confined to kitchen tasks. Beside her, rendered with exquisite and perfect vision... are four fish, some papery-skinned garlic roots and two gleaming eggs. There is a background scene of *Christ in the House of Mary and Martha*... The light in the painting comes from the still life of fish, roots and eggs. This too has been said to be of emblematic significance... It doesn't feel like that when we look. Martha and Mary were emblems of the material and the spiritual life – Martha in the Bible is "cumbered with much serving" and resents the contemplative Mary's inactivity... The authority of the painting is in the mystery of the represented things. There is the sense that this painting is a claim on behalf of the beauty – the divinity – of the stuff of life, of Martha's realm.'

Might this be a realm we can discover in our novels, too? That may, as in painting, have been present all along if only we look in a different way? Could it be that those qualities we seek out in a still life are also soothingly present in the busiest of narratives?

Certainly the greatest books are becalmed upon moments that don't seem so important, that don't necessarily add up to anything in terms of narrative development, that can almost just seem to be there for their own sake. We don't mark them for that reason. Quietness, after all, doesn't *do* anything, and domestic intimacy easily disappears into the bigger themes and concerns of the novel. Certainly, in terms of the way we talk about, read and review novels, they could be almost invisible, these other, quieter parts of the story. Yet how they do carry the weight of, as Byatt says, 'the stuff of life'. In George Eliot's *Middlemarch* the formidable Dorothea takes time out from considering her destiny, turns for a minute away from the whirring machine of character and incident that is that mighty novel, to have a brief exchange with her sister:

'Now, really, Dodo,' said Celia, with rather a deeper guttural than usual, 'you *are* contradictory: first one thing and then another. You used to submit to Mr Casaubon quite shamefully: I think you would have given up ever coming to see me if he had asked you.'

'Of course I submitted to him, because it was my duty; it was my feeling for him,' said Dorothea, looking through the prism of her tears.

'Then why can't you think it your duty to submit a little to what James wishes?' said Celia, with a sense of stringency in her argument. 'Because he only wishes what is for your own good. And, of course, men know best about everything, except what women know better.'

Dorothea laughed and forgot her tears.

'Well, I mean about babies and those things,' explained Celia. 'I should not give up to James when I knew he was wrong, as you used to do to Mr Casaubon.'

The complexity of this little passage, the density of meaning it contains, is all through *Middlemarch*, of course, but in a novel with so much going on, what is interesting in the scenes between the two sisters, in particular, and adds further richness to that complexity, is the fact that Eliot makes them so very slight. They're over in seconds, the interchanges between the two women, they could almost seem frivolous. Here, Celia makes that throwaway-sounding remark towards the end, 'babies and those things'. It's almost as if Eliot dare not give anything else to the exchange to have it settle in our minds. We think Celia doesn't add up to much because she's given such feminine asides, often she plays with her baby while she talks, gives her serious elder sister a darling little nickname. But in that 'deeper guttural than usual' is the authority of intimacy that comes from outside the novel — from the sisters' shared history, childhood, home. And how it leaps at us, 'guttural'. But then Eliot has Dorothea laugh, as though her very allusion to that other invisible place embarrasses by how much honesty it forces: that these slight scenes with the sisters tucked away in a room together may well carry more insight into character and motive than the page after page that surrounds them in her big 'big book'.

To what extent, then, may the quietness of the ordinary — here the day-to-day, unremarkable relationship between two sisters — have been rubbed out of importance simply because so much of it concerns, as it were, 'Martha's realm'? In *A Room of One's Own*, Virginia Woolf wrote of the necessity of writing that covers all aspects of our lives, and of women, in particular, making the subject of what they know an honourable and serious one for proper literature. That's not to say these would be 'women's books'. On the contrary: 'I would ask you to write all kinds of books, hesitating at no subject however trivial or however vast... What is meant by reality? It would seem to be something very erratic, very undependable... It lights up a room and stamps some casual saying... Now the writer, I think, has the chance to live more than other people in the presence of this reality.'

Such reality, though, continues to elude us. Though the shelves of memoirs and autobiographies and diaries are fully stocked with books on the life of the stay-at-home, books that take the ordinary at-home life of parenting and housework, birthing and babies and the school run, it is rarely granted full-blown status as a subject entire in itself. As an ever-extending theme for long column inches in our daily papers and weekend supplements maybe, as the stuff and stuffing of a certain kind of chick-lit, too, it may form a kind of bulk... But in serious literary fiction the ordinariness of the life at home, the cups and saucers of it, is seriously lacking. As we saw in *Middlemarch*, it is present in glanced moments, asides, but does not dare press itself fully upon our immediate consciousness.

Raymond Carver does much to redress the situation. He is positively inspired by the subject of the mundane, celebrating the lives, invisible and for the most part non-eventful, that so many of us lead. His perfect short stories mostly take place inside houses and rooms. Here are husbands and wives closed off together in the sealed chamber of marriage and household drudgery, yet through the cleanness of Carver's sentences, by the way he manages the apparent banality of his prose, its flatness and even spacing of punctuation, the domestic is transformed into the existential. In 'Whoever Was Using this Bed', a husband and wife are woken in the middle of the night by the telephone's ring and can't get back to sleep again:

> She leans over and covers her face with her hands and begins to cry. I move down there to the foot of the bed and sit beside her. I take her hand and hold it in my lap. I put my arm around her. We're sitting together looking at the headboard and at the nightstand. The clock's there, too, and beside the

clock a few magazines and a paperback. We're sitting on the part of the bed where we keep our feet when we sleep. It looks like whoever was using this bed left in a hurry. I know I won't ever look at this bed again without remembering it like this. We're into something now, but I don't know what, exactly.

Considered in this light, Carver is less of a 'Dirty Realist' (the appellation under which he and a number of his contemporaries were gathered by *Granta* magazine in the 1980s) than a suburban purist. Just because a subject doesn't have grand ambitions or sweep doesn't make it, as the moniker suggests, low-down or somehow 'cowboy'. Realism can be as much about dishwashers and your wife posting a note under your study door to tell you she's leaving you (in one of Carver's most dramatic, mysterious stories, 'Blackbird Pie') as it need be about cattle-grazing and shotguns. Thomas McGuane and Richard Ford and Bobbie Ann Mason and the rest of the 'Dirty Realists', maybe. Not Carver, with his kitchens and yard sales and unmade beds.

But Carver wrote short stories, and, as Chekhov showed us from the start, short stories have always been a comfortable home for writing about home. Many of James Kelman's perfectly ordinary tales of making tea and turning on the electric fire come into the same camp. It's only in the novel where the front door seems to get slammed shut. Judging by the reception of *MotherKind*, a novel exclusively concerned with the reality of mothering and care-taking at home, Jayne Anne Phillips must have heard the sound as loudly as the famous door banging closed in Ibsen's play. The difference being that in *A Doll's House* Nora leaves the home behind her in the final scene and thereby gains fame and notoriety with her theatre audiences, while for Phillips, because she's opening the door again and walking back inside, she ends up closing it behind her. The sound of it shutting is the sound of exclusion.

So the cups and bowls of milk, to return to A. S. Byatt's metaphor of the domestic in painting, instead of being in sight of our gaze, are painted over with the dark of blindness. The ordinary is shunted away from us as though it doesn't even exist. After all, what goes on behind the closed doors of domestic life, the housework and child-rearing, does not have a voice economically or politically; we should therefore hardly be surprised that it does not make it itself any more publicly known in the grand halls that contain 'big novels'.

And yet, for so many of us, this is where we live, behind that door, amidst the dirty dishes and the infant clothes that need to be washed and washed that are the stuff and article of *MotherKind*. Can we not transform that reality into a way of seeing instead of denying its existence? Recognize that this life, the life at home, may be as wondrous as the grand romance or tumbling narrative? Can we not train ourselves, as Byatt when she looks at those pictures has, to see afresh, see anew? As she remarks at the close of her piece, when writing about an installation in metal of what seems to be an ordinary bag full of rubbish, *Bag 9* by Turk, 'The bin liner is the apotheosis of looking.'

6

Lesley's Tables

Certain things in this old world continue, they shine through:
iced white and yellow jam-filled cakes for birthdays, for example,
they will do, and chisel-toed and tissue-wrapped new pairs of too
expensive brand-new shoes... And getting off the plane at Inverness
will make it on this list, and getting off at New York City too...
But up there with them, breaking with the rest (like breaking open
envelopes with invitations or with cheques inside or waking early
with the children tumbled sleeping in the bed with you) is
'Lesley's Tables'.

'Lesley's Tables' is the call that's first of all, or the message on the
phone that goes, 'Oh hi, I'm thinking... Bill and I were... Are you free?'
And lunchtime it might be or dinner, 'Can you come? I'll make some

food. Say Friday, 8-ish? Will that do? Or Sunday, early in the afternoon?'
And you, your heart lifts outwards, sits somehow complete, just like
the loaf of bread that sits upon the tablecloth beside the wine, 'Of course!'
you say and can't stop smiling then, no matter what's just happened or
been said in life, 'I'd love to!' Then, of course, you do, you go — and what
old kind of magic

does continue, is accomplished then in Lesley's kitchen, in that room,
is managed in the midst of all of time's bleak rush, like all the pasts,
the jokes, the babies who've been born and grown are there at once,
made present at one table... Fraser in her high chair, I can see, and just
last week, is how it seems, and Lewis in his paper nap and doddering,
walking, trying to at least, towards 'Dave Graham', I remember, and him
saying later, oh that little boy is *sweet*!... And Millie, in her sleepsuit, also,
for one dinner, and that lunch when Harvey somewhat gallantly showed
Katherine his room

(in his husky voice at three, 'You want to come upstairs?') — all this
my dear, dear friend to celebrate, make words for you, for all your tables,
all your times... and Christine's deep inside them too. So let's make trumpets
from infinity to sound, and golden rows of bugles and of horns... Let's

cry into the blue with Christine's dying, 'Life!', the life of food and friends
and tables, Lesley, your own tables, spread and welcoming and ever new…
So, no matter creeping comes old death to take us, still we gather in our
hearts around the bread and water and the wine, and there, you see
are Christine's matches on the table

too – remind us that some things continue, they shine through: Lesley opening
up the door to greet us, wild and blonde and wearing some black thing
that's floaty, maybe something new, a scarlet lipstick, glitter on her eyelids
last time, I can see it, it's a groovy sparkly greeny glitter blue. 'Come in!'
she says, and all of us, and Christine too, we endlessly will enter, like
no time has passed at all, we do, we come, we gather round your table,
held for now, forever in this certain mood – the wine cork pops and all our
aching yesterdays forgotten, turned into this all present *now*. 'Ah, Lesley,'
said Christine, quite recently this was:

'She's something, Lesley. And those parties that she has – Oh boy…'
And Lesley, it is true.

7

Coming Down off the Hill

Thinking about how stories come to be made out of little things that happen, things that don't necessarily seem to mean much in real time but come to add up, somehow... Well, it makes me consider. This one particular day I'm thinking of, for example, and whether it was really like that, then, with that feeling of intensity around those few hours, I can't say. But it started off, the mood I'm trying to get into here, on a Saturday, around dawn.

It was winter, and early enough for the three of us, believe me, when what we'd been up to the night before was staying way too long in some bar Nick loved, lining up the empty glasses. Chaddy was driving. I don't know why. The old North Road was always going to be way too twisty and dark for him and he worse on liquor, holding to himself the memory of the night before, much closer than Nick or I ever would... I should have been doing that part, at least. But the three of us were tired and not thinking straight from being up so late — because how else do you get around the news of a sudden death? Any death, but this in particular, someone your own age who dies out in the paddock with an old man's heart, the sun on him, the wind, and down he goes? That's what we thought. For while it was irresponsibility of the highest order to be hung over and weird as we were, in our black clothes but tatty, my dress not even ironed, and Chaddy driving while it was still dark — I have to say it was normal, too. To be that way. Three of Andrew's supposed 'friends' and we couldn't get past ourselves enough, even with funeral cake and flowers, for five minutes, not for five minutes. I look back at that now and can only think I must have been someone who wasn't paying enough attention. That I didn't know how.

Andrew's death, you see, when we set off that morning was not the thing here — which sounds awful, I know, but really, the big send-off at the farm, the wintry light, cold grass and the shape of a box cut out of the ground... These were not the key images of the day. What I was thinking about, rather, from first thing in the morning, was Chaddy going on and on in the bar the night before, poking about in his glass for the olive. 'I feel I should be doing something,' he was saying, repeating himself, but the words building to some kind of a statement. 'I feel there should be a way of making the choices that are available to us moral, you know? Important.' He was pretty drunk from early on. From the minute I'd got off the plane he'd been full of this place he and Nick wanted to take me to, the waitresses would be cool and weren't we going to have just a great time there, we three? We'd be not thinking, he said, not thinking. Yet here he was, off on these big themes, pretty much since the moment we sat down, he couldn't stop himself. 'Choices really do carry the difference between good and bad behaviour,' something like that. 'It's not just about a diversion. It should be important, what we do.'

I think this is what he said. It was a subject he couldn't let go of, probably coming out of Andrew's death, about not being married, not having children. 'I want to take a stand that people don't laugh at me, because I know they laugh at me,' he said. 'People think my life's some kind of a joke.' I don't know. 'I could say the same thing,' I said right back to him, 'all of us have put things off.' And Nick joined in, 'Easy, Chaddy boy. The aisle's not the only path for lovers...'

I'm just representing here, of course. Nick's dark hair falling over his eye. My hand on Chaddy's knee. Him balancing on that narrow bar stool, throwing back his head at some point to sing some sentimental old Irish song about a boy martyr who got hung. But responsibilities, seriousness, these were the ideas being put about for the night. How to live, you know. Be decent. Order Martinis and not think about Andrew at all.

'Maybe we should get a pet,' I said. 'If we're going to go down that sort of track.'

'Yeah, that's a responsibility.' Nick looked at me and smiled. 'How about I'll be your pet and you can be responsible for me...'

He tried to put his head in my lap like he might be a little pet, a little dog or a kitten, but it was difficult in that bar that was so damn hip you couldn't even sit properly.

'You guys okay?' one of the waitresses kept saying.

Chaddy's song was stringing along, his eyes were closed.

'Oh, we're okay.'

'Come on sweetheart,' Nick said to me. 'Mia-*ow*...'

Something like that. I'm putting speech marks around sentences to make them more dramatic off the page, but the fact is none of us in that car had exactly made it on the Big Success front. The only difference with me was that I was the woman, so I'd left. I'd put miles between myself and that place where we all grew up. I'd stayed away. But then, I came back, too, didn't I? I always came back to those two in the end. Only for a week or so at a time, okay, but still... The three of us whenever we were together again was always like nothing had ever changed. Nick on his charity gig, Chaddy at the paper. It was a little time-lock, being back with the two of them. Nick would be with his beloved Fathers at the People's House as long as he breathed... And my other boy, no better off. Sure, he had the book column, that at least took him into the world... But Chaddy. The old *Saturday Herald*. Really, what a stint. And stuck in the entertainment section now, no longer a part of the paper just for books, that must break his heart. Yet in this, really, who am I to judge? I just write my ads at the agency when I go in there and nothing so fancy going on with me I could mention. At least Nick was driving the bus, taking them off to the seaside, those poor sick kids he looked after, or getting them to the hospital for their appointments, whatever. And Chaddy was turning up for work with his book bag each day. What was going on so large in my life I could sit by and judge them? Here we were just the same, the three of us ended up in the dark that was there around us. Coming down off the hill that early in the morning on our way to Andrew's, putting Andrew in the ground.

Nick said, 'I've an idea Andrew would have it written down somewhere to be buried in the morning. Last big joke. He'd know it would really put us out, get us up this early to drive up here. Who made these roads? It's covered wagon time, my children...' He laughed his dry laugh. 'Hell, I might try the same trick myself when I am gone. Arrange proceedings for an 8 a.m. send-off Saturday morning, no, make it Sunday. Give the mourners one big long weekend to drink the bars dry in my memory then get them up at dawn to go grave-digging...' He shook his head. 'I need to close my eyes,' he said. 'I'm still drunk. We need coffee. Whisky. Whisky in the coffee...'

'I've packed a thermos,' I said, and with his eyes closed he smiled, patted me on the knee.

'Good girl,' he said.

The bush felt close to the road. In that early dawn it felt very close, and wet, like it would have things in it that were asleep now but would soon be stirring. The earth and clay the plants and low trees and scrub grew out of was cold on the north side of the hill, cold clay and last to get the morning light, dawn coming up at our back. Sun wouldn't show on our faces. There was a scent of mulch of leaves and moss, but not decomposition like we'd be able to smell it if it was summer, coming down that road as I always used to smell it through the open windows of the car... As I said before, I was the one who should have been driving.

I forgot about it when I was away, but coming back it pressed in like those dark leaves were pressing in, that I knew that road so well. Coming down to where the land flattened out, where Andrew's family still farmed, to the houses where they still lived... It had been my parents' place, too. Even though it was a long time ago the old Beauly station got sold up on my mother's side and my father's family's horses and that land... A hundred million years ago, it may as well have been; still, it felt like coming down was making some kind of a return. Even though when we used to come here in the summer we no longer had a house there, and by now my parents had been gone from that old flat-plains land such a long, long time… Still. Here I was. And I knew all the people we were going to see that day, all the aunts and uncles, all those people of Andrew's, and he had a lot of people. And I knew the smell and the dark as we drove as a familiar, particular memory. At the end of it, of the three in the car, I was the one wearing the black dress. I was the one coming home.

Earlier, in the car, we'd had the radio on. Nick had been singing.

It's impossible,
To think that you would love me, it's
impossible.
To think that you
would smile at me,
impossible…

Chaddy had said, 'Turn that off.' He couldn't concentrate, and I think he thought Nick and I might start something. 'I hate

Frank Sinatra anyway,' he said. 'He can't sing.' It turned into an argument that was old, that went on a lot when I wasn't there, I think, about what was good and wasn't good and why – was it Frank Sinatra or Bing Crosby, Titian or Poussin? – that was to do, actually, with the way the two of them loved each other... For now, though, after a stab at it, they let it go. For my part, I was still high enough I could have let my behaviour fall either way, towards either of them – but I let that go, too. The funeral dress was making me feel old, so what was I possibly going to do in it anyway? Seduce somebody? Act like my mother, still kicking around the place in high-heeled shoes? So I said, 'It's impossible,' just like Frank, instead, and Nick leaned forward and turned off the radio.

'You're impossible,' said Chaddy, and he was cross, looking at me in the rear-view mirror, that the two of us were in the back together, that he had to be driving, that he'd had to be the boring one who needed the radio off. 'You are,' he said.

The road wound and turned. All my childhood I went up one side of that hill, came down the other – my summers, my mother's summers. Her family were all Beauly, Beauly people knew each other. So coming to Andrew's funeral... His family, my family... It was more than homecoming, actually. I don't even know why I just wrote that before in that simple way. How could I be 'coming home', with my family split and spread, my mother up north by now in some motel, most likely, drinking herself to death with one or another old boy who'd been handsome in his youth, and my dad gone? No, it was more to do with the bit of the cemetery that had our family's names on it just the same as it had Andrew's. All my mother's family, as I said. And my dad, she'd met my dad in that little place. Something about that. The way Beauly got to you, is what my mother always told me.

The night before, and it wasn't even the night before because we'd taken ourselves right through, Chaddy had ended with crying in the bar. He'd put his head into his hands, as though doing some kind of an act, but this was real. He was weeping, rummaging his face with his hands. Then he put his forehead down on the wood of the bar.

'I hate it,' he was saying, and then he looked up and I knew what was coming, where all the other talk had been leading, from the moment he looked up at me and I saw the expression on his face. 'I hate it that I have no part to play,' he said. 'That I'm worthless, in this world, this society, to you...' It was that again. His ruined eyes were all red and streaked with messy tears as they looked into my eyes. Of course, I had to turn away. 'To you,' he said. 'Why don't you look at me? Look at me...'

'I don't want to look at you,' I said. I remember exactly. I wasn't crying myself. I didn't want to look at his crying face.

'Take it easy, mate,' Nick said to him then. ''For Christ's sake, we've got a funeral to go to. You need to cheer up.'

Chaddy tossed his head; he made a sound like a little horse.

'Steady,' Nick said.

'Why should I? Why should I?'

'I said, *steady*.'

It was the way the two of them were together, I mentioned it before. Chaddy's emotion, full like flowers held in Nick's light grasp – a bouquet he could just as easily give away, toss to some girl, some little bride-to-be. The way he reduced Chaddy's terrors, made small the blooms of his grief and turned them into petals that would scatter in the air.

'Don't make a bloody drama of a classical education,' Nick

said to him. He shook a cigarette out of a pack and Chaddy took it from him. Nick lit it. 'You've just been wrecked by Homer and the rest,' he said. 'Forget about it. We've all got stung in the neck at some point by the damn gods. The Big Boy Himself. A Catholic upbringing's no worse than any other. And besides. We're smarter than most people...'

Chaddy smiled a half smile then, looked back at him. It had worked, is what it seemed, feeling taken up and thrown away, the petals were drifting. But then he said, 'No. We're not clever at all...' He took a quick puff of his cigarette, like a teenager, or a child. 'To be this unhappy, right now, this drunk, on this sort of self-soaked misery, that's not clever. I'm not even crying for someone who's dead, so what does that make me? A man who only cries for himself...'

'Well, your classical education's lost you there,' I said. 'You should have empathy, like this...' and I took his hand then, and I don't know what I was doing, I placed it under my shirt, on my breast.

As I said, I don't know what I was doing. I was the person, remember, who couldn't look into another's eyes. The one who sat with those two for hours in that bar, put on the black dress, but later, at some point will catch a plane, go away. And maybe it is starting to come together now, the little things. The queasiness that came with the driving, bad driving and the hills, the curving road and what was coming up, Beauly and Andrew, the night before... No wonder I was sickened. It was like everything I did was gestures, gestures. Yet, the light still managed to come up at our back, behind Chaddy's mother's car, behind my wretched dress. And after the empty night, the long hours of dark and sleeplessness, we did the thing, came down off the hill into the beautiful early morning winter day.

And Christ, but it was lovely, to see it all there before us, this place in the world. The frost was lain upon all the pale green paddocks, but lifting in white sheets of cloud and frozen air and rising into a pale blue sky. The trees stood bare in orchards with low walls and gates for animals to pass through; in the distance were the mountains with their snow. The sun rose and rose, made gold the frost and whiteness, like a cloth spun through with threads of gold, seemed all the colours, and we drove down, we drove down on the long thin road through the village of

Beauly and beyond to where the houses turned to farms, the farms to open fields, and then there the gate of the McPhersons was before us and we turned into the drive.

There were cars parked like for the Beauly Races all around the house, down the side of the house to the back, to the end of the drive. We found a space down by the tree Andrew and I had made a fort in when we were nine and slept out in, and I opened the door and there was that smell of grass and frost and running outside in your bare feet down the road to get the milk, that perfect first day of the holidays smell, and I got out of the car and Chaddy and Nick got out and we walked towards the house.

People were standing through the hall and down into the kitchen, and in the kitchen there were more people and some of them were making eggs and coffee, or pretending to, but mostly everyone was drinking. We'd stopped for my thermos before, so we'd settled ourselves on that front, but still there were the big bottles of gin and bourbon sitting around on the counter-tops, Andrew's dad coming up saying, 'Good to see you,' and clapping me on the back, pointing to the table where the whisky was. 'Good of you to come...'

He didn't look old, Rob McPherson, or any less tall, to me, than he'd always been. Even with his son dead, actually he looked taller that day, with the kitchen so full up with people, and I recognized some of them, a lot of them, from way back, and other people too, friends of Andrew's from university, but mostly Beauly people, and my cousins, aunts and the McPhersons. No one looked well. They had that kind of puffiness as though they'd just got off a long-haul flight, and some had dark glasses on, and some of the women really did look like they had been crying, but on the whole you couldn't tell. Certainly, you couldn't tell if Andrew's dad had ever been. 'Just help yourself,' he said about the whisky. He tapped me on the shoulder. 'Good to see you,' he said again. Then he disappeared out into the hall. I could hear his big voice: 'Everyone all right? Fixed for what you need? We'll be leaving in about half an hour, the service starts...' Nick slipped his own dark glasses out of his suit-jacket pocket, put them on.

I looked around for Andrew's mother but she was nowhere to be seen. Nor was Andrew's wife, Caroline; she wasn't in the kitchen either. I went into the bathroom and splashed water on my face and from out of my bag got the little toothbrush. You'd pretty well be certain Nick and Chaddy hadn't thought of such a thing, but after last night I was not going to take any chances I'd be like this musty-smelling old loser now I was back on my home country. I looked in the mirror and scrunched up my face a bit; it was okay. Toothbrush, water on the face... That's what women do who aren't married when they go to funerals, they go to the bathroom and get themselves clean. Last night... Forget last night. I didn't kiss him, didn't trace his lips with my forefinger, but I'd taken his hand and placed it on the skin over my heart and I never should have done that, used him that way when it was Andrew I was trying not to think of, trying not to think of him... I never should have done that other thing at all.

Rob had said it wasn't long until the service, and in the time leading up to it I don't think I've ever seen so many people at Beauly before, cars on the roads, people walking. The little turn-off into the church was jammed. The light stayed perfect, all day there was that sun and a bright wind that kept the edges of things hard. Later, when we were at the graveside, I remember looking up and seeing the trees shifting against the blue sky and it was like their leaves were made of glass. Andrew's wife and the children, her and Andrew's children, stood beside the mound of dug earth, the pit, and for one crazy minute I thought the hard wind was going to knock them all straight down into the hole. In church, they'd had to be taken out. When the priest started talking about Andrew, and who he was leaving behind, Caroline had let out a cry, it wasn't hysterical, but more like she was cross with him, with the priest. 'No!' she cried out, and then again 'No! No!' and then it did become real crying, and the little baby she was holding started crying too. It was when the priest said, 'These two young people had a life together,' talking in that soft Irish way. I didn't know who the priest was. Father Donnell had left years ago, and this one was much younger than him, but he had the same gentle, sweet voice and it was when he used — and perhaps this was the first time Caroline had heard it — the past tense, that she cried out that way. Someone said later it was because the drugs hadn't worked. Andrew's mother just took her arm, led her out, with the baby. And then she came back for the little children who were left in the front row, Andrew's son and his two daughters, who were staring straight ahead, facing the front of the church where the coffin was; she whispered something to them and they turned and went with her back down the aisle out of the church.

All of this, writing it down, to use the words of my own father, was 'a damn shame'. It's what he would have said if he'd been there. Though he wasn't ever really Beauly, not in the way my mother was, he loved it, that light of Beauly, that long wind. He loved raising his horses there, the McPhersons, Andrew's dad, he loved Andrew. He would have known a lot of people that day, my father, as would my mother, if my mother had anything left to her by now that could recognize other people — as being someone other than herself, I mean — she would have seen too and known well many of the people who were there.

The wake was going to go and go. There was all that parking around the front of the house from the morning and then at the back the home-paddock gate was off at its hinges to let more cars in. They just kept pulling in, one after another. By now, the people I'd remembered from earlier had disappeared into the general crowd. I caught glimpses of this person or that, there were bits of talk, but it was like a cocktail party — *Oh you did know him at school, well, in that case you'll remember…* A lot of people asking about my mother. I'd been expecting that, that was okay, and there were a lot of people saying how much they missed my dad, and, of course, talking about me and Andrew. There was Chaddy, I saw, and Nick was with him, over at the bar refilling. 'How you bearing up?' he said to me at one point. 'These people are all your family, aren't they?'

It was Andrew's dad who suggested we just get the hell out. There was no end to the thing otherwise, as I said, you could see that coming a mile off, for a long time there wouldn't be. No wonder Susan wasn't there. Apart from the short time by the graveside, I never really saw Susan at all. The death party had become just that, just a whole lot of people standing around drinking and talking – and really, what was she going to do? Hand out plates of sandwiches with one of the catering girls? Say, 'Here, try one of these'? Andrew was her child, her only son, he was a kind of an angel after all. I hadn't seen him for so very long, but in that time between university and now he'd married, had children, he'd taken over his family's land, made his father's life his own, been a father himself as well as a son, a husband, a man who'd had so much love around him, so many people who needed to be in his presence... No wonder his wife couldn't stay in the church. Or his mother be able to stand square in the rooms of her home...

As Rob said, why not just get the hell out?

There was an olive grove, he said, something Andrew had started and we should go there, use the house Andrew and Caroline had been working on restoring there, we could spend the night. 'We miss you, you know,' Rob said to me. I don't know why that should come to him now. 'You and Andrew... You should be staying with us tonight, sweetheart, that's where you should be. Where you should have always been. But you see how it is...' He waved his arms around the sitting room, doors open, people spilled out onto the terrace and everywhere people, people... 'Get out to the grove and relax,' he said, something like. 'Andrew would want that... I know he would.'

He hugged me then, a quick hug that was more like a tight grip, like holding on. I'd never been in that sort of a situation before in Beauly. Then he told Chaddy how to get there, these long detailed instructions, and he was saying, 'It's open, you don't need a key, we never lock things up around here,' and pointing to me, 'she knows that, though she might act like she's forgotten...' He was, I see now, writing this, of course, trying to stop himself from breaking down. He was trying to be strong, and that's okay, that's okay. 'Don't worry,' Chaddy said, 'we'll find it.'

It turned out to be about three miles out of town. I drove. The other two were going for it straight out of a bottle in the back seat but I was through with all of that by now. Rob had told us to head north and we did, watch out for a long broken fence after you crossed the river, and I saw the broken fence, and you turn left there after it ends, and you'll see the trees then, the opening in the break, and that's the entrance there. 'It's pretty straightforward. It's easy.'

Is what he said. But I had no preparation for the place in my mind, so when we got there I was aghast. Late afternoon and the sun had softened by then, melded, and I saw that the land we'd been directed towards was where I was from. The boundary ran off by the back way of my mother's father's old property and now, being here, coming into it this way, it all fell about me in a rush and I remembered it, remembered my grandfather, and my mother when she'd still been living there with him, with my dad, and being a child and playing there myself when my mother was younger and everything was different and we had somewhere we belonged. Yet how the place was also changed. For where once there'd been scrub pasture for sheep and cattle, ridges of macrocarpa and pine, now all beyond the boundary wire were new trees that Andrew had planted and smooth grass, and none of the trees was higher than a young girl. I stopped the car at the entrance to the gate and got out. In the back seat they'd fallen asleep. I left the keys in the ignition for them to find when they woke up and walked into my mother's land, my darling Andrew's land. Just to see where I had come to.

There must have been a hundred of those girl trees, a hundred of them. Planted in a circular pattern, with great order, a beautiful thoughtfulness of precision, each spaced exactly proportionate to its neighbour. All of them the same height, coming to my waist, their branches about them with their tiny buds of fruit. I walked into them and I was like a giant amongst them, going through that low plantation like entering into a maze, and I was surrounded by the bodies, arms, of trees. I didn't know what I was doing, walking deeper and deeper in. These trees were someone else's, their life, their planning, their planting, the hard little olives, their idea coming to fruition... I had no business being there. I was walking about them like an owner, but an impostor, for I had gone away and I could not return. I had nothing here. I had made it that way, that I would have nothing. Made it that I would become someone with nothing to leave behind her so that when she returned there'd be nothing left for her to find.

Still I continued to walk through the little trees. Still I brushed with my hands their soft green branches. The sky deepened, darkened, and I couldn't stop moving amongst them, then at some point, with the wind still present in that landscape, I lay down.

I must have slept. Because when I woke bright lights came out of the dark to show where the house was. The windows were all lit up against the night. It was an easy thing to walk towards that brightness. The door was open and Chaddy and Nick were inside; they'd sobered up by now, they'd built a fire, there was the smell of cooking, soup maybe, it was warm. When I walked in the door they stood up and there was something I couldn't bear in the way they came to me. Was I so very cold? Had I been outside so long asleep in the dark orchard that it set my body shivering the way it did when I reached the warmth? Was I so exhausted, by the day, the night, the people I had seen, the things I had done? I don't know, but here is the fact of it – my truth, what I am left with here, at the end of this day, this page of words – that I could barely let them come to me as I approached, that I could barely allow it as they put their arms around me, drew me in.

8

Annunciation

You just uncurled your hand
and look! There's something there.
But what? A bit, a scrap, a little mark
is what you saw, it's mud, perhaps,
you think, a fleck of dark like earth
or crumb of something stuck, a piece
of leaf or insect's wing

or stain of pen from words that you'd
just written on a card, Miss D — but no,
for it's most definitely caught and
fixed there now upon your skin and held
by sweat, the heat that throbs out from

from your blood, a 'something else'
that stays there on your palm.

But what is it? This tiny thing? Unnoticed almost, nearly, really not quite
there, but hey, it's there all right, a mark
that you most surely never had expected.
Just a dot maybe, but real, this fragment of
rich clay or element from moisture in the air,
a particle of this wide world

and owned this moment to uncurl your
hand and see there, you two, on your own —
and look again! It's not so dark, no, after all,
the fitting of this tiny form upon you, light
it is, like thinnest metal beat to film,
like mica or like gold... It's gold, it's true,
is what it is:

the colour of the halo of announcement.
That soft rich and precious flake of treasure

rivers can't undo or fade, the brightness
looked for ever in prospectors' pans, it's gold,
it's gold. The thing you never knew you had,
infinity is made from it, like halos' crowns
and rings,

the small forevers that we wear, reminders
of what comes to us unbidden... soft, soft gold.
And to have it married into our dim skin
we want to marvel at the fact, the miracle,
the angel's touch... A fleck of now's
tomorrow lightly held... Is what *you* had.
For just

one moment maybe but was there, infinity
was there, its mark, though rubbed through
now, remains: the memory of gold forever
from that moment when you did uncurl your hand
and saw: *Hello. It's you that I've been holding,*
come to me unnoticed while I was standing
here.

9

Leaves

Untended we
must have been,
bedded deep our roots
maybe, and put in pretty pots
our mothers would have chosen, had
their hands about us, sure, as we did start to grow,
and were pruned a little at the start, and fed, but then,
some point, our gardeners put the pots
upon the sill and turned,
walked out
the door.

The leaves
they'd helped develop,

all the stalks and twigs... We grew just fine
out there in the weather (though we weren't the kinds
of plants intended in that way, to be outdoors and go unmanaged,
yes, *unmanaged*, yes, these are the words, *untended*, un-cut-back
— you know?) And now I see how that lush green... It may
have been too much, sometimes, for plants
so meant to be
inside
and safe.

Yet every
year the pots
are out there in the air.
The rain falls down and sun comes or
the dark, or else it's cold... Stuff happens (like
the weather) yet we did it, somehow, managed, wore
our flowers, toughened up our stems to hold the further growth,
broke back the stalks that could not bear the weight of any
more new leaves, shed seeds, had buds
that turned
to fruit...

And all of it

untended, *wild*

is how we must have

seemed, in those days, to

the rest, I mean — the mothers of our friends, the aunts,

the daughters, plants still sitting pretty in a row and here's this

different species doing all this crazed untidy growing on her own,

and so near to all the others but apart, a pane of glass between

to stop the inside and the outside touching...

Different kinds of leaves.

No mulch

dug in,

or peat:

the earth

that we'd been given

had to be enough. We willed it, made it that

the first and newly potted shape would last us, that

container hold. A garden's how it had to be, a whole wide plot

of trees and borders in that pot, a definition that we could defy and be

defiant of ('What? This small thing? Of course, it's fine! Why ever

should it not have been?')... And so it still goes on, we *flourish*,
last so well
upon the sill,

through all
the seasons
grow. We keep on
growing, never had the knack to be in care —
that's a lesson now that's late to learn — for we don't really know
what it may mean to let ourselves be managed by another's hands. We do it,
in the end, ourselves because we've always done it in that way: just grow.
Just come up through the seasons, girl. Never, ever go inside... Our mothers
fixed it for us in that way, began the work that we continue
on our own
to finish.

And these
new roots
set down beside us now
in their own pots, are out here with us, grow
themselves beside our shade of leaves, the tangle of our planty branches

and just look at them! They're strong, accustomed in their green, their sap,
their seeds, to snuggle up beside us but still push beyond, to take the
rain upon them, put their tiny branches into air... And that other
gardener who was there
(— and who
was she?)

is long gone
now, and unknown
to our small plantings here.
Just memory is left of her, her hands
about us as she put us gently in the earth, the sense of
(and you write this in your letter) *scent*, a fragrance of her, or a scrap
of song... All we have left, and that word for her, the word we hear ourselves in
Mum, my daughters call me, *Mutti*'s what it is for you... It's *mother*, yes, to that
extent we're all together here and planted on the shelf. So when we say 'untended',
really what we mean's the same, one word,
the name: *myself.*

10

Domesticity in Literature:
Women at Home in the Novel

Domesticity has always been quietly present in literature. There are the kitchens and dining rooms, elaborate set pieces written around mealtimes and the planning of parties. There the row of beds in the nursery, nanny sitting in her chair... All are the emblems of home-life that accessorize the dramas that play out in the pages of our books. Think of the glorious hominess that enriches and pacifies the turbulence of drama and war in Tolstoy's great novels: Natasha nursing her new baby at the end of *War and Peace*; Kitty and Levin in *Anna Karenina* playing a quiet game of cards on a winter's night. The same peaceful scenes, moments of calm by the fireside, gild the darkness in *Jane Eyre* and are the chapter ends throughout Austen, giving us pause before the next letter arrives from a potential suitor to bring on the plot.

But as I've noted (in Domesticity in Literature: The Art of the Ordinary), that's where fiction keeps them, as moments, scenes. Compared to the grandiosity of the novel's ambition, the blasts of high drama sounded by the canon, it's too quiet, this life at home. We want stories, after all, 'big books' — it's one of those standard measures of praise we apply when going through the prize round-ups and must-read lists. And while the domestic may be used as a setting it's rarely more, a backdrop, a jumping-off place into a more vivid and more 'interesting' world. Kate Chopin's *The Awakening*, a classic piece of early feminist writing about a woman waking up in the morning and deciding she's going to leave everything she thought was important, her husband, her family, her home... is a fine example of just that. Home is the place you leave.

It's not surprising, of course, when women, in particular, have struggled for so long to free themselves from what they came to see as the captivity of home and sink and endless drudgery, that fiction would want to escape out the window. For many, 'home' means 'jail'. Yet for those who have chosen to stay at home and have the babies, look after husbands and wives and families, the domestic world is a place not of limitation but of other, different possibilities.

Take Carol Shields's latest novel, for example. *Unless* is settled properly around the domestic with a protagonist who writes and thinks while she hoovers and cares for her family. Though *Unless* is more widely known as the story of a girl who leaves home to sit on a street corner with a sign around her neck saying 'Goodness', I would still argue that it's the life at home that fills up its pages. It is at its most powerful while the dishwasher runs or the family stirs in their beds. One early morning Norah surprises her mother by returning home from her student flat:

> I loved her sleepy, yawning, mussed look, merging with what I
> thought of as the careless use of herself in the world... For the
> moment, though, she was home; I had her to myself. She was
> wearing one of my cast-off robes that zipped up the front,
> that awful burgundy colour, her body lending grace to the
> awkward lines. But I was suddenly alerted to something about

her presence: the fact that her face looked oddly fallen. Her eyes were swollen, filled, though not with tears. What I glimpsed there was something hard, fixed, chitinous. What was it? 'We are real only in our moment of recognition' — who said that? I was recognising something now. I put on my reading glasses and looked at my daughter again, closely... She shrugged and made a grab for my waistline, just hooked her thumb over the belt of my robe and hung on, with her forehead pressed into my stomach. I would give anything to have that moment back.

That perfect clinch Shields achieves here, recognition, the connection of birth that is alluded to in all the bodily detail — 'stomach', 'swollen', 'chitinous', 'her sleepy, yawning, mussed look' — is wonderfully managed. So why then couldn't the daughter be leaving her mother to go on holiday with her boyfriend, or to go... anywhere, rather than make that rather grandiose dramatic exit to a street corner and martyrdom? Shields's *au point* writing could surely still engender the same deep feeling of loss in a mother for her baby grown up. But in the end, it's as though the author doesn't trust the 'moment of recognition' that she has most beautifully established as being enough. So she seems to exchange the deep, true theme of her novel — the intimacies of family life — in return for one that satisfies the conventions of narrative. And it is that narrative, not the other, that critics and reviewers remember. That narrative becomes the way we read.

Another Canadian, Alice Munro, is similarly regarded. A recent article in the *New York Times* quotes a memorable line from Munro to sum up her work (regular collections of stories since 1979): 'dull, simple, amazing and unfathomable — deep caves paved with kitchen linoleum' — and certainly the domestic life of women is predominant in her fiction. But actually it is the manipulation of that subject that is Munro's real interest. It has often been remarked that her short stories are like novels in miniature, and certainly what is foremost in our minds when we read her is the tension between the smallness, the familiar Chekhovian short-story world of home-life that is depicted, and the grand sweep of time and action that the narrative covers, that has all the scale, the what-next?-ness, of the novel.

Her latest collection, *Runaway*, features as a kind of trilogy three stories that arc the life of Juliet, as intellectual, mother, daughter, lover, friend. It features Munro's signature authorial manipulation perfectly with phrases like,

'Never tell that to anybody.' (Actually, she did tell it, a few years later, to a woman named Christa whose name she did not yet know.)

or,

'This was a letter that Juliet found years later.'

The story is full of stories, characters that intermesh, letters that remark on the actions that take place in the present or past and then comment on them. A suicide takes place in the middle of a train journey, and Juliet,

got out her notebook and on one of its ruled pages began to write a letter to her parents:

…We sat around there for ten or fifteen minutes and then started up again, and I could see the engine rounding a curve up ahead, and then suddenly there was a sort of Awful Thump…

…But as soon as she had written the words *Awful Thump* she found herself unable to go on. Unable, in her customary language, to go on.

Customary language – the language we are used to – custom, habit, familiarity: this is the domestic ground in which Munro's fiction is planted. The above is a drama embedded within another, more dominant story about Juliet's marriage and family. But that subject is never her subject entire either. Munro's wives and mothers are not, in the end, rooted in. Always there are possible escapes and freedoms. They don't stay at home that way.

The wide-open world is an attractive place and, of course, we will always need access to it. The history of the English novel is all about whether we remain where we are or move on – from Robinson Crusoe discharged from the safety of home onto his shipwreck island, right up to Jonathan Franzen's minutely examined family refrigerator representing all that is stifling and suffocating about staying put there. But if we are to agree that, as the painter Robert Motherwell suggested, we 'embrace the native and the foreign with the same spirit of enquiry', then we must surely celebrate, along with the writers of adventure and wide-open spaces, those whose subject is wholeheartedly located behind the closed doors of home, whose pages reflect the lives so many of us have chosen to embrace.

These lives on the whole would be women's lives because it is the women who still, through choice or necessity, end up at home. And there are three writers working now who are distinctive in their placing of the domestic at the moral centre and principal site of action in their books, who site women at home as their subject entire. In this country we have Tessa Hadley and Helen Simpson and in America there is Jayne Anne Phillips's *MotherKind*.

In *MotherKind*, Jayne Anne Phillips, an acclaimed, prize-winning writer in her own country, still not properly and widely known this side of the Atlantic, writes with close attention about the sensuous closed-off world of parenting, establishing as her main theme what it is to carry, bear, nurse a child. Phillips takes a concentrated pull on a subject that, in terms of literary fiction, is more or less invisible... And then explodes it into revelation, that this kind, mother love, may be the most potent of all:

> Ravenous, Kate knew, this need to birth babies, to hold one's
> child. The fact was, birth dwarfed sex, swept sex before it.
> A woman had sex to get this, to be here, to smell the clean
> smell of her child tended by her hands, to drink him in,
> consumed. Kate sometimes imagined herself a flat meadow;
> for years she'd avoided babies, which was easy, because most
> women she knew didn't have them. Most women thought they
> were looking for men, not babies. Kate thought now that
> they were wrong: they were all looking for babies...

While there are endless memoirs given over to babies and birthing, this is the only work in English I know of that achieves the ravishing transforming effects of literature on that subject. Consider that open-mouthed 'Ravenous', followed by its steady iambic, the pulse of repetition. Here is the experience of reading an idea insisted on by rhythm, the pace of the words like the race of the heart, bringing on the rounded feeling of thought and apprehension turned together into language.

Certainly, it's possible to see why many readers — some men, say, and some of those without children — may find the subject troubling. But good writing insists on its subject in a way bad or simply mediocre writing does not. And besides, isn't 'troubling' interesting? As I've already mentioned, *MotherKind* failed to achieve the readership it deserved because of this very subject — 'the cracked nipple novel', one male publisher quipped. Though without doubt, in Phillips's writing, mothering becomes not a female but a literary subject, it seems the idea persists that life at home as a subject entire is just not that interesting.

On this side of the Atlantic, Tessa Hadley and Helen Simpson are tackling the same prejudice. Hadley writes novels and stories about wives and mothers who move within the confines of a domestic locus and whose lives are made larger, more interesting, because of, not in spite of, the choices they have made. In her first novel, *Accidents in the Home*, Hadley actually sets up the premise of the external 'exciting' world being more interesting

than the stay-at-home one — and then, piece by piece, disman-
tles it. Her two main characters are Clare, wife and mum, and
Helly, her exotic and fashionably dressed oldest friend. How
dull Clare feels herself to be, at the beginning of the book, as
Helly swans into her cramped terraced house in a swathe of
green, mirror-embroidered velvet, her groovy boyfriend carrying the bags:

> When they all kissed, the Londoners smelled expensively of
> bathrooms full of bottles and scents and lotions, and Clare
> was aware of her limp T-shirt which had soaked up the smells
> of the onion soup she was making for their lunch. The
> onion soup, with parmesan toasts baked in the oven, would
> be delicious (it was). And Helly couldn't cook. But Clare felt
> that everything brilliant and savoury about her might have
> appeared to have drained into that onion soup, leaving her
> wan and dull and domesticated.

Certainly, we may feel like we're on familiar ground here — the
subject of a woman sweating away by the Aga and feeling second-

rate is, after all, bread and butter to most of our columnists and the whole Aga-saga pop-lit genre. The difference is, though, that those writers are ultimately striking a pose that is cynical and ironic. Tessa Hadley's Clare, by contrast, as with all her women, is a creature of literature. She goes beyond striking a pose to grapple with the reality, and self-denigration gives way to questioning, thoughtfulness, insight. Domesticity is both the surface that she cracks and the depths beneath it:

> She sat on the stone steps with her novel turned face down beside her because she couldn't concentrate on it. This was one of those moments given on earth like a promise of what's possible: the palely veiled creamy blue sky, the water glinting, the sunwarmed stone against her skin, the heat on her shoulders, the loved child playing happy in the earth, all the loved family spread safely and at their proper distances like a constellation, so that she, in her place, was part of it, holding and held. In literature though, Clare thought, there is a notorious problem with heavenly peace. It is well known that it can only be appreciated through the glass of loss.

Her second novel, *Everything Will be All Right*, picks up the theme that women and their families have lives, balancing work and home, or simply being at home, that are as interesting as any other in literature. Once again Hadley buffs the so-called 'dull' to a beautiful sheen. In one exhilarating scene, Joyce, who has given up ideas of being an artist in order to look after her painter husband and their children, and who has turned her aesthetic sense into a real pleasure in decorating her houses, confirms, during a dinner party she's hosting, that her husband's been having an affair. She walks off in disgust into the night, planning an affair of her own, but then returns at daybreak. 'Her head felt clear, she was perfectly well...' Hadley writes. She considers her husband's paintings, their marriage. His work is more mature, worth her attention, she decides. She analyses her relationship to him, what the affair may have represented. She's intelligent, sensitive — triumphant. An individual who can marshal emotion and objectivity both and turn them to her moral gain. Then she does the dishes.

Hadley's novels, and her short stories that inhabit the same space, sing out for us to attend to the sink and sitting room as

places where literature can flourish. Making the ordinary gasp —
that's what Hadley does. She continues the story of domesticity
that begins where so many of the love stories end. In a short
story of hers, 'The Surrogate', there is this perfect follow-on to
the 'Reader, I married him' scenario:

> I love Patrick. I think we're well matched. But of course I'm
> not infatuated with him anymore. You can't go on being
> infatuated with someone you share toothpaste with, whose
> crusty inside-out balls of socks you have to put in the washing
> machine. I still count on his intelligence and his articulate
> way of speaking. But I get irritated at the way he gulps in a
> breath of air just before he pours out some hoarded-up
> information, and the way he guides conversations around to
> an opportunity for him to be surprised at someone else's
> ignorance.

Saying the unsayable, the unsaid... Flaubert's *Madame Bovary*
caused a stir for all the same reasons. Not that the work even
need be as shocking as breaking open certain taboos. Hadley

purposefully plays down drama in order to show ordinary activity and thinking. That way she has us attend to the biggest drama of all, the mighty stirring that can take place — while we mop the floor, or feed a child — within our head: 'But of course I'm not infatuated with him anymore.' Perhaps it's what Charlotte Brontë was striving for in the end. Put the two phrases together and read them side by side and now I hear they hit the exact same note.

Helen Simpson is the other writer in this country who's offering us literature with the same possibilities of vision. Her second collection of interweaving short stories, *Hey Yeah Right Get a Life* (which, as with Munro's triptych of interconnected characters, has all the reach and range of a novel), takes the suburban and, in particular, the strains and pulls of motherhood, as her subject. In the title story a woman besieged by offspring, vaguely condescended to by her husband (he wants her to make more of an effort with her appearance, with her ability to keep up with things), is fully enmeshed by domestic life, yet is also in love with it, impassioned by it in a way other characters who appear in the same collection, who live and work outside the home, are not.

Simpson doesn't just write about how it appears to be a wife and mother. She doesn't just write about its effects. She writes about how it *feels*. There's a sense here, amongst the sorting of the dirty laundry, of a character exultant, soaring, alive, which a moment with a toddler reveals:

> Abruptly she put the iron down on its heel and swooped down on him, scooped him up and buried her nose in his neck with throaty, growling noises. He huffed and shouted and laughed as they swayed struggling by the vegetable rack. She tickled him and they sank down to the lino laughing and shouting, then he rubbed his barely-there velvet nose against hers, gazing in without shame or constraint.

Where, outside those final pages in *War and Peace* with Natasha and her babies do we read such gorgeous celebration, delight, in maternal love? And why are there not more books like this? Or like *MotherKind*? We do have to wonder, in the eighty years since *A Room of One's Own*, what has become of Virginia Woolf's exhortation that we 'write all kinds of books, hesitating at no subject, no matter how trivial'? She points out how the habits of the past inform the present, and how masculine values prevail: 'Speaking crudely, football and sport are "important"; the worship of fashion, the buying of clothes "trivial". And these values are inevitably transferred from life to fiction. This is an important book, the critic assumes, because it deals with war. This is an insignificant book because it deals with the feelings of women in a drawing room.'

Has anything really changed? We may admit Raymond Carver's suburban houses and Frank Bascombe's quiet ruminations about home-life and houses in Richard Ford's two follow-on novels from the celebrated *The Sportswriter*... But there are lots of men in those books to carry the themes, and men tend to dominate the narrative. It seems it's a man's world after all, and Carver and Ford can write about sitting in the kitchen in a way that's not viewed as being insubstantial in the slightest.

Yet reading is about inclusiveness, expansion — and literature has always shown it can accommodate a changing rota of subjects. Why not, then, allow the place that for so many of us takes up so much of our lives to become pages, chapters, books? This place of dirty dishes and children's cries, love and loss, and hope and despair... To let the ordinariness of it through, to allow as a right and proper choice of subject the known-ness of the known... That would be a true expression of how far we have come, readers and writers, men and women. Then, as George Eliot wrote: 'If we had a keen vision and a feeling of all ordinary human life, it would be like hearing the grass grow and the squirrel's heart beat, and we should die of that roar which lies on the other side of silence.'

11

Katherine — Still

(FOR DAVID)

Come clattering softly in
then, come on, pony, little
cat, or you be Pippin that
sweet dog who's on TV,
come on. Come *in*, and
now for goodness' sake, just
curve yourself, all rounded back
and thumb suck in and fit
yourself into us just like that,
your poor old mum and dad...

You fitted once entire between us,
turned and settled then with

sucking thumb and buttock
roll, the lift I felt within me
those last months I carried you,
my captain, cargo and my
passenger at sea, you little girl,
and the turn of your back then,
that rolling on the sea of me and
Katherine, now you're three...

And look at you, your father can't
contain you any more, his tears pricked sharp
this morning, hard to leave you
at the nursery door... So now, of course,
come in, *come in*. Not any
other creature, not the cat or dog or
thing that's on TV, just Katherine,
just 'me!'. The girl a thought or dream
has startled into waking now...
Come clattering softly in

and stay.

12

Armature

A thing exists
inside a form of clay, say, it may be, or
plaster, I suppose,
a thing that's fixed,
is nailed (if wood) or soldered fast, it's
'armature,' you said, and I said
'What?' and you said, 'armature,'
again, 'the base, you know, that I can use
to work upon, to sculpt around,
to lay the clay down on, a body
or the shape
of what I want
to make.'

The rain
came down, we sat there in your car, and then
you talked about
a piece of wood
you'd had made up in just this way: a
cross-beam, kind of, backbone, arms, I guess, a bit
that jutted out, and that would be the head
from there, for you
would wrap some wire
around it's what
you said, and I
kept thinking

'Armature'
— that word. I'd never heard of it
before, like armour
I first thought, but no,
for this is all within, this certain shape, a
structure, like a skeleton, like bone,
but no again, there's bone but bone can

yield, as mothers know, that feeling of
our own bones easing open to
accommodate
the growing shapes of
babies' heads and
arms and legs...

So no, this
not like that for this
won't move at all,
this certainty within, this wood
and nail that's hammered to the spot, long
known, so strong it's stronger than ourselves, than
scaffolding of bone, a thing that's been from
the beginning: will. Is what it is.
I see it now, the will towards
a shape, a self, the start,
of all the work,
beginning, there

and felt

deep in

like knowledge, memory: *who we are*

and always have been:

this, this thing.

This underlying pinning into place, the never moving while

the shifting happens all around it, wrap

of wire and slip of clay,

but still it stays and

waits, before the

babies or the

love, or hope

or grief or

loss...

The thing

that's set beneath, that no one can imagine

or can see, the thing

that's never touched

or burned or broken, never come apart. And we,
we branch out from it with our wire
and clay, and you say,
as the rain hits down
that this piece you're
working on, this 'woman', when
she's finished will
be cast
in bronze…

And I know
where she's come from now and how
she's made. You
said the word yourself
that holds her steady as you work, and start to push the forehead,
in, or build the neck or breasts… You know the word, you've
taught the word to me as we sat talking
in the rain and all the air
outside the car,

it's armature, ourselves,

what's kept of us

within and known and guarded, *armature*, a force unmoving,

always there.

13

Oh, Veronica!

It's all there, somehow, in that 'Oh'!
Your widened eyes and open smile,
your breathless, restless sense of fun —
the way (and is this true or do I think it so,
because of that same wondrous 'Oh!'?) you
hug your knees when you sit talking, listening...
Do you do that? Oh, Veronica

I think you do! I remember when I first
met you coming through the door down off the street —
it was the eighties then, and winter, bang! The front
door closed and you were there with Cappy too,
your scarves and wool against the cold,

and I said 'Hi' and you said then, the way you said it (Oh!
The Oh!'s there in it too, the word) 'Hell – oh!'

You do! Veronica! You do! You have such big Oh!s in you!
Excitement, joy and love, like open arms the way you
talk, with laughter there inside your words like
energy inside the vowels, 'Oh, Yes!' you say. 'Oh no!'
And asking always questions (Irmi's there, inside the rhythm
of that phrase) and listening for the answer,
your head to one side, the chop of your dark hair, or

your hand straight up into the air that night in San Francisco
when you came to my reading and when the Questions? came,
the Comments from the Floor? you had questions right away and
things to say and then we went to dinner, you and Cappy, David and me
and David went off to have a pee and you said Oh! Then too,
Veronica, the minute he was gone, Oh! David's wonderful! You said
and we talked that night about love and families and how you loved Irene...

So Oh! Oh! Oh! Veronica, just Oh! It's you.
Your work, your words, and just some little moments

I have had, I guess, to know you in and yet they add, they grow
and seem to have such weight and bulk and truth it's like
a lifetime's friendship there, to form a shape inside my head
that quickly moves into my heart: your mother's daughter,
sister to Irene, aunt to those two swingin' girls... Is how I

know you, what a gift, to come inside the circle of your
'Oh', Veronica.
Thank you.
Yes.
And Happy, Happy Birthday
too, Happy Birthday dear Veronica to
You!

14

How Do I Begin to Say?

How do I begin, Irene, to start with this?
A poem, kind of's what I'm trying for and yet
the things I see are colours, lights and sounds,
not words, but bowls and wood and silks and
plants, the sky, the Cape, pale grasses, gems,
the stillness, beauty
of your smile.

So, how do I begin in words? It does seem though
the time is now to try: you make these books for
everyone, Veronica and Irmi and the girls, and I,
you know, I want to make a page for you. For YOU!
My dear Irene, life's colour and its

light, heart's beat and inspiration...
You!

I found myself, the other day, with Katherine
in a shop just down the road and seeing there
these children's things, these bowls and plates and cups
all shades of pink, from rose to dark to creamy pale,
and so we chose some, Little Peach and I,
mixed up the colours, and that
night

as I served supper to the girls I saw myself as you,
delight in that same riot of the colour, saying, 'this way?'
'that way?' as I moved the plates around
to match or not to match, and placed the cream
mid-pinkness to the dark, like berries there, or lipstick
— I don't know — and laughing, kind of, as
I did it, no

not laughing, like a chuckle, more it was, this kind of
glee, Irene, and coming straight online somehow

from your Manhattan kitchen into mine, this
joyfulness, this pleasure in the sense, the moment,
this, this piece of loveliness in time, and yes,
I know too, how this comes with something
more

like steely feel for beauty too, perfection, and it's
hard, I know it is, to want to always make it, have it
right, exact... I feel that too. Just this weekend
when asking David (hanging pictures in our hall)
just to change the nail 'three-quarters of an inch from there',
and move it to the left, he raged back 'Kirsty! Don't! No one
will see!'

So I got on the ladder then, of course, I had to, just
to get it right, just to shift the fraction that so matters,
yes it matters, of course it does... And this to say again,
and how to say (I've done it poorly in these stories)
how it comes from you, Irene, or more, that what you've
given is... you've named my world, your thoughts and gestures,
lit it,

showed the way, you make sense of all the colours...
The woman who is like no other in my life: whose high
regard for all that's beauty and necessity and truth,
has taught me (when there was no other who could teach me)
what it was to be a woman, wife, a mother, how to *live*
and raise the daughters, make the choices we might have
to make...

The woman who talks long into the nights and days,
apartment and her flowers shining out around her,
scarves and silvery earrings, hands that make their patterns
in the air, her dancer's gestures there, all elegance and
light and grace, and everywhere she touches... Beauty.
Who's some slim years beyond me and is who I
need to see

as proof that gorgeousness goes on and on and on...
So how, you know, can I begin, Irene? To tell you
all these things? (my father, when he met you, straight away
could see the signs...) I needed you: the woman who is you,

a woman stepped clear out of air and full of music, painting,
and New York, the woman who I'd needed all along and no one
else will do...

It's you, Irene. The gift, the smile, the word, the light, the
tulip in the vase, to fill the space my mother left but more
than this by far because of who you are, yourself, and how
do I begin but start at the beginning with the name *Irene*.
It's you.

15

Sweeping Up Stars

Not perhaps so strange, or so bizarre
that I should find myself
again down on my knees
and sweeping up
with dustpan and with brush
the crazed remains
of yet another
afternoon
of glitter and of glue
and paint, the craft
of your inventions, girls,
the 'let's-make-cards!' beginnings

or the 'why-not-paint-today?' exertions

of a certain kind of grey-lit hour,

the time when we've a while yet

till it's tea,

and lunch, the park's long gone...

It's only

you two here

and me — and makes me think,

you know, consider, just how many

afternoons of this

will I have left

in one small life,

amidst the tax returns and supermarket shops

and work not done and stuff that I'm aware I should

be doing now while on my knees in some strange

corner of the room... That I'll not have

much more

of this, the chance

to gather in

the bits of glitter, sweep up brightness
from the floor, to tip into the bin
bright constellations... How much time
to sweep up stars?

16

The Pass

Certain roads, you get to a part of them, turn a corner, say, come over some kind of a hill, and you feel… There's no going back. Like you have no choice, the road there to take you, and all you can imagine is the way ahead, who'll be there, who's waiting. Callum Sutherland, he'll be like me enough that way. A man in his car now, coming along this exact same piece of road I'm thinking about and it's early morning, a grey light up here and cold, but look at the place, darling, all around you. You can't help but see it, sitting forward slightly in the seat of your car, and that road a thin dark strip with the soft land falling away like blankets on either side.

Bealach Nam Drumochta. 'How was it, the Pass?' that's what everyone says to folk who've come over, the aunts, the cousins, the people you know. Someone in the pub at Rogart, in the midst of a high summer, although there were winds, so asking 'Drumochta, coming over today, in all this air? You managed all right?' Oh yes, I managed, they're always asking me the same and I live up here, but you've never said anything — have you, Callum? — about the feeling of excitement with the journey, as the car comes up through the country, deeper in. They'd think it queer if you talked that way, and besides, what right do you have to claim that kind of attachment when you've never stayed here any length of time, weren't born here? You probably think you shouldn't have such emotion for a place when it's where you've come for your holidays is all.

Still, he's switched the headlights off five minutes or so ago to let himself see the land, the pale colours. Though it seems flat, there's a sense of an approaching, the summit, Bealach, like the aunts and uncles talk about, this rising, broadening, so the further you go the more you can see of the distance, and off there somewhere in it, up ahead, the house.

Callum...

You've no choice in this, have you? It wasn't me, though, who telephoned your mother to say your father was back. But now she knows he's up here, she's set herself to worrying about him, I can see. Calling you at work, I suppose: 'Your father,' and that quick way of hers of talking. 'They've told me at the house he's up there again. Been there a while but not taking his pills so now they're worried enough to let me know…'

Callum.

'These people…' she would have said that, too. 'How can you get through to these people? I want you to go up there, Cal. To bring him back and I'll take him for a while.'

And you must have nodded, said something, yes, that she could barely hear. 'Of course, if you really think –'

'I do think.'

So the road tilts as though to let him, ease him towards the place… He's got to do this, got to. But now that he's here again, it feels like there's something in it that's of his own choice after all, this journey. The incline increases, but gradually, you'd hardly even know you'd come up a mountain pass it's so slow, and now the day is lifting, you know, I think it's like everything else has slipped away. The wife in bed with him this morning in the dark, the two boys in their room. The street lights and the oily wet of the road where he lives, pulling the car out of the drive...

Something about the light does it, works this kind of spell. Approaching the Bealach, he looks out and it's as though the entire sky of the world is open, poured out, let loose all down upon the hills. Like there was never such a thing as darkness here, like there could be no darkness, only this bare, clear air. There are the clean open flats of the moors, pale grey and dun and heather streaked with dark and peat, and blackish watery burns, some places coming down cut with broken stones, rocks, and all of it, the sweet land, available to you somehow, that sense of reaching out to it like you might take it, be able to gather it into yourself and make it yours, a universe of endless land and sky and distance, and pick out the mountains for your stars.

But it's the road that keeps him from disappearing. The grey of it, and thin, with no place much for passing. Since childhood, the memory's been in Callum of all the years, coming along here with his father, lagging behind caravans or estates hitching trailers, or boats, and his father's frustration, *Christ, get a move on, man!* His hands gripping the wheel, and those eyes of his trained on distance. First Drumochta. Then Bonar Bridge. Dornoch... All the places he was wanting to get past, to get through, to get *there*... And terrifying, I know myself, that cry of his: *Christ!* Like the man would himself put a sword through Christ's side. Callum could see it all, as a boy. His father's profile as he sat beside him in the car, seeing his father out the side of his eye, not daring to say a word, not wanting to breathe even. And where was his mother then? It was always only ever him making the journey with his father, enduring that silence of his, or the frightening cries, and the sense of him, that man in the car beside him, the sense of him wanting out, into the hills and the water, seeming to be pushing him along, pulling him, great pieces of the sound of the place unfurling in his mind, like a *pìobaireachd* you might think of it, like there may as well be someone coming down off the hills now with a set of pipes to call him in.

It's going to take a couple more hours to get up to us here, much easier now than back in the old days; still, the particular emotion that comes whenever he thinks about his father, the house that is so surely his house, is starting up in Callum by now. Like his father's passed it on to him, old country, like new country, all green, grey-green, and a dwelling place that stands alone amongst the emptiness, that feels for all the world like your beginning and your end, your birthplace and where you go back to, again and again, to find the things you left behind, and where you would also want to go, in the end, to die.

So...

It's all here all right, all of it coming piling in. Now he's approaching the Pass and it's been a few years, sure, since he was last along and so the roads may be better than before and faster with the new bridges and all change still... The view in the windscreen's the same. And out to the sides... He's still his father's son in this, being here, like he's a boy again and nothing's changed. Same scrawny, scaredy kid coming up through Inverness and Ross, all the way up into the hills you had to go then, to the bridge before you could come wide again and back down onto the coast. He used to get sick on it always, that bit of the road, and on the long rounding part of the ascent that's behind him now, thank God it is. He still has the memory of the churning in his stomach, coming down into Golspie, too, remember, the sick taste in your mouth, but at least you were nearly there.

His father stopping for a whisky then. Always it was the same. The hotel bar at the Royal, and *Not much more in it now*, his father's words as he drew the car up outside. He would go straight in and Callum used to sit on the grass outside, a bottle of pop, maybe, something to take up the time, otherwise just sitting on through the long summer's afternoon, into evening, and his father happier, Callum could hear it, through the open window of the bar, in his voice. He'd be talking by then, his real language, not about money or business or what he might have read in the papers... There were snatches of it earlier, in the car. 'Aye' instead of 'Yes', little pieces of the Gaelic... But it was now, when he got up here, in the Royal, back in the Highlands where he'd been born, like an animal come in off the cold hills to a place where it knew it would be safe, that you could really hear the difference, Callum could. His father talking as himself again, now he was back, his language the language and tone and music of the place where he needed to be.

The day is fully arrived on the journey now, the grey rain-pelt of the morning's drive sliced down the centre, like a fish opened clean out of the water and the red of the sun and gold coming through it and it's how it begins, for the man, Callum Sutherland, now he's at the Pass and over it, something starting for him here. Like a story beginning, but not a story, for I know the people I'm writing of, I've been told the details of all that happens here, or I know about the facts first-hand — but a story all the same in that it needs someone to tell it, make something of it, too, the fact of this returning. Certain roads, you get to a part of them... Remember? And there's no going back. This road become the only road and the season, early winter, the only season. The further north he drives, the colder it is and the light, the big fish laid out glistening and new... A sense of something torn open to show the day in it. This day. Every minute it seems to enlarge around the car, the road, the lovely man.

For all that, the large sense of his journey here — sense of destiny, you might call it — and the urgency of his mother's call, Callum takes his time arriving. Having stopped off, finding himself waiting, hanging back, at the garage where he lingers for petrol, water... Checking the tyres. Buying some food, fruit, sandwiches, a coffee that he drinks right there in the forecourt, leaning up against the side of his car, reading over the headlines in the papers bound up outside, looking at advertisements for chocolate and lottery tickets and cigarettes. Time, more time. Then, he leaves, at last he leaves from there, driving some more, stopping some more, at the side of the road, twice, just before Tain, trying to call the house on the mobile phone on the clear open bit of the road there, but of course there's no reception, then again, later at the pub in Rogart, going into the bar, but nobody he knows or recognizes, still... He found himself anyhow taking a seat at the bar, buying a beer, and then another...

So that finally when he gets up the road and turns off into the farm track it's late afternoon and the light's near gone. Here's the sky that's been all around him from dawn to long morning and silver-grey, clouded as it was back over the Firth but with a kind of a sun in it beneath the cloud... Since then, leaving Rogart, all that's been getting darker, and darker still, so all he sees as he drives the long narrow track to the House now is the peaty bank cut in deep either side, reflected back in the car's headlights as black welts in the heathery dark-grey land.

He turns the final corner and sees it, the old place. We've the lights on in the side lodge where we live, my mother, Iain and myself, but the house itself, its peaked gables, is practically in darkness, only one room with a window that is bright. I can see how it appears to him, how it might seem impossible to him that we might live here, in the midst of all this emptiness and, when he turns off the car's lights and sees it, the sky. As though how can anyone live here, make a home here? And yet we do, my mother and Iain and I. Working here, managing the animals for the old man, the river here, the land... It's what we do, our family, what we've always done. For us it's always been the House, 'Falabh'. The 'Nowhere', it is in the Gaelic, Aiete Aon Arech, the End of the Road, and the road does end here. There's nowhere else to go.

My mother's at the door in the time it's taken to turn into the driveway. He switches off the engine and there's her form against the rectangle of light behind her.

'We thought it would be today you'd come,' she says to him as he gets out of the car and approaches her.

'Hello, Margaret.'

Nothing about her's changed he can see, though it's been a good five, six years. He takes her hand, gives her the customary kiss upon the cheek and she says straight away: 'Your father's been waiting.'

The dogs in the kennels up behind the generator have started barking from the minute they heard the car arriving. Of course, it's because they'll be remembering, some of the older ones, his smell, his voice. The sound of them gets louder, more frantic, now he's out of the car. *Let me out!* They seem to be crying out to him, exciting the others to do the same, thrashing themselves up against the wire-meshing of their pens. 'How is he?' Callum starts to say, but Margaret's pulling him inside against the cold and the noise. *Please! Let me out! Please!* She closes the door behind him.

'He's... You'll see for yourself.'

It's warm inside. Callum sets down his bag.

'Not just himself,' my mother says, 'that's what Iain thinks, but that might just be with him not taking the pills... Helen —'

'What?'

'Helen thinks we might be losing him. That he's ready. He's sleeping, you know, a lot of the time... Or he wants to be outside and we have to keep bringing him in. It's been bitter cold here. We've already had some snow...'

By now they're inside the little kitchen where her husband's sitting at the table, cleaning the guns, a bottle of whisky, a tumbler, set before him. He looks up at Callum, nods.

'Callum.'

'Iain.'

There's a pause, there's always a pause. Like the drive up here, like all of it, nothing changed, everything just the same, only his father, this time...

'How are you, Iain?' Callum says anyway. 'You're well? Things have been going okay?'

'Okay enough,' Iain says. He takes up a cloth and wipes down the butt of a rifle, puts it down again, slowly unscrewing the cap from a bottle of oil.

'Your father's not been too good.'

'Yes, if there's —'

'Aye, well then...' Iain continues with his work. 'You'll manage as you can, I suppose.'

'I suppose...'

Callum does what he always does now, when he's back here with us, with Margaret, my mother, and Iain, whom everyone calls my father though he's not my father at all. He'll stand, for a time, certain words exchanged. Iain will offer him a dram, he'll say, thanks, but later maybe, and then my mother will take him through to the main house, to the small sitting room where his father will be.

This time, though, my mother does not take him. He goes down the hall by himself to where the old man is waiting, sitting in his armchair by the fire, alone. My mother busies herself in the kitchen, heats through soup, rolls, puts the water on to boil for tea. When I come down from my bedroom to take the things through she's away upstairs herself and Callum's sitting in the chair before his father, his father not saying a word. The lamps are on, and the fire's bright this darkish afternoon with snow in the air and still one or two old dogs barking, poor beasts, not understanding why it is they've not been allowed to see him, to come rushing in and fall upon Callum to lick him all over his hands. They know all right that it's my brother who is here.

But it's not for me to go and release them. I set the tray down on the small table by the window and Callum says, 'Hello, Helen,' then, and I turn to him. For the first time in a long time I'm looking on his face again.

Then his father speaks, 'He took his time getting back to us, Helen, didn't he? Our boy?'

He smiles, first time I've seen the old man smile since he's been back up here, a smile, a real smile. He takes a sip from his dram.

'Don't think I'm going back with you, though,' he says. 'Callum. I'll not, and you should know this fine, I'll not be taken.'

'Dad...' Callum says. 'Hello...'

It's as though there's light all around the pair of them. I can see it, in this room with its deep wooden walls and windows set, this late afternoon, with all the little panes of glass. To see them, together again, my father and my brother, these men who, though they will never know it, have a daughter and a sister, too...

'That'll be all, I think, Helen,' the old man says then. 'You can leave us now. Tell Iain we'll not be needing the guns in the morning...'

And I turn to go. Leave them, the one facing the other, by the fire I set this morning. 'Wish your mother goodnight from me,' my father says to me as I go out the door, back into the dark hall, yet with the sense of light, this gorgeous piece of light still present with me, at my back. From this man who's come from where he was, come up that long road that's behind him, crossed the Pass, and returned to us, to Nowhere, 'Falabh'. Our Aiete Aon Arech, our End of the Road. Our home.

17

Poem for Katherine

(GOING TO NURSERY FULL-TIME AT THREE AND A HALF YEARS)

The horses made no sound this morning,
nor the carriages or cannon, nor the bugles and the men,
for you were not there to see them,
little girl.
The start of all your leavings
started then.

18

A Woman in a Bedroom

'Keep it like a secret, hold,'
you said, 'it here,' and fisted up your
hand into a ball against your belly
as you spoke. 'Just keep it safe, don't
talk of it, don't tell a soul, it's yours,
and now is not the time to speak about
the work that you have made.'
With that, I like to write, you crossed the floor,
went over to your bedroom door and opened it
and stepped inside...

I like to write — for really, we full know, don't we,
we two, that that is not what happened then?

(We have these conversations all
the time while drinking tea and crunching
down those biscuits that we like, while
speaking in a rush our thoughts and
listening hard before the children ask
for juice or help to cut a paper or to glue or
watch them while they're running
or they want to sip our tea... Or else
we're talking on the phone and one
of us is driving (or the other) — badly
(in my case) or (if it's you) too fast...

Yet even so I like to write you saying all
that stuff for me just then, about the holding
in of art, of words, and balling up your hand
for strength before you go into your bedroom
where your own most private work is
thought about and formed...
For there, just look! Thick leaves of paper
with your marks are pinned and wild all on

the walls, the carpet smudged with pastels
and the smell of linseed and of oils, and
canvases with colours laid down thick
like questions (so they seem to me, right now,
like red: 'Do I make sense?' says red, 'can I be
blue here for a bit?', 'And I, oh am I any good at all?'
asks black — another poem, that)... And this,
this place where you have gone, it is...

Your bedroom, you tall woman!
Bedroom — and no bed is there! No
dressing table, mirror, and no clothes
that I can see, a bedroom full of paint
and thoughts put down as colours and
as lines... And now, okay, I know (I
like to write) it's not the same, you've
moved into another space, a studio that's
up the road and all your things are
there that you will need...

But still, tall paint-marked painter, maker, mother
(inspiration in my current work and friend)
your bedroom as it was back then and you
— the present you — they hold together
proudly and as one: a tall and gracious figure
in a room that's meant for rest (and here for her's
no glass to see herself, no pillow for her head)
…A bedroom and a woman in it, painting,
thinking, drawing, and uncertain, yet in that
uncertainty alive, her marks come true:
the image fixed. The words are you.

 'Be private and be strong,' is what you said.
A woman in a bedroom with no bed.

19

'She Knows'

She did that thing she always did, of making him feel he was the only one. Like the whole deal was hers, the party, yanking open the door and welcoming him in.

'You! You're here!'

There was the smile, the hair…

'This is wonderful!' like she was in some kind of a big show. 'You never come out!'

'And yet…' he said.

'Here you are!'

And she took him by the hand and led him in.

'Actually,' he said then, 'I came to see you.'

'Liar!'

'No, seriously.' He stopped, resisted. 'I need to talk to you, Marianne. It's about Martin. I knew I'd find you here and –'

'Oh, Robert...' She smiled at him, looking at him with her head on one side, and there it was again, with her saying his name, the whole thing starting up again, really, it was like a show, and she the star in it, that great switch of her caramel-coloured hair shaken back off her shoulders, turning so she could present herself to him that way... *Oh, Robert...* Hooking her arms around him and drawing him in close then so she could kiss him, in that place that he loved at the side of his neck...

'No!'

He pulled back, away from her properly this time. He was not getting into all that. To talk about Martin, okay, he could be with her now, but nothing else, just nothing. Besides, it was Alistair's party. He was here to see Alistair, the reason after all, Alistair's play going straight into the West End – and yes, Marianne, maybe, but really he was here for Alistair. To wish him well. Have a drink with him, say, *Well done*. Just the two of them, Robert and Alistair, then he would leave. Otherwise, Marianne was right, he'd never come out.

'So did you get my message?' he started to say, but she wasn't looking at him. 'Course I did. For God's sake, Robert. Stop going on...' She was unbuttoning his coat. 'There are millions of great people here,' she said, 'why does it have to be blah, blah, blah, that old subject, all over again? He's fine. He's a little boy. You're a great father. Stop worrying, I told you. Here...' She had the last button loosed from the heavy fabric, her arms were bare. 'Let me take this from you now,' she said, pulling the whole thing from him. 'Otherwise you're never going to stay, I know it.'

He stood, let her, the garment feeling suddenly heavy on his body, so yes, she could remove it. There were the bare arms, his coat in her arms, and her legs were bare too, Robert saw, no tights or shoes on — nothing new there, of course — just those jingly things on her ankles that she'd picked up in India last time, one of those 'research' trips, the stuff she loved to run around in.

But don't get into all of that now.

Instead he tried again. 'I really do need to know what you think,' he said. 'Can't we talk about the school idea, at least?

His teacher says the timing is critical. This is important, Marianne.'

But she was just bundling his coat up to take away, laughing at something someone else had said, and, in a way, what was he trying for? Already she'd done the thing. The party, the coat she now held in her arms... Making all of it into hers and nothing he could do to change it, the old feelings back for Robert and lit up and burning. The burn on the side of his neck from the kiss, foolish airlessness in his chest, like he was the child here, this not about their son at all, but he the one and she could do anything with him she wanted, start over, come home with him, be together again like they'd been together before, anything.

As always, it surprised him. The reaction, it shouldn't still work that way, but something about Marianne always had been there... Like now, going off and putting his coat away and what had taken place in these last few moments between them, the feelings she'd started up for him, like nothing for her, while he was left with them, sensations formed into emotions and thoughts that came straight out of the past and interfering with

everything else. All that he tried to think about or do or say...
After nearly four years of separation she could still stop him,
leave him standing in hallways, waiting on the next move, then
come back out for him like now, emerging from some room of
Alistair's as though the house belonged to her, or she was a lover
of the house's owner, or a most intimate lodger there. Saying,
'Right, first things first. First drinks, then Alistair...' taking his
hand. 'He's going to be over the moon that you're here, my
love,' and all he could do was let his hand be taken, follow, as
Marianne said to him, 'Come this way, with me.'

The place was full. There were people everywhere, standing,
pressing in, and just to move through to the dining room where
the drinks were laid out on one of the big tables... It was an
effort, of course it was. With Martin at home, right now sitting
up in bed, letting Mrs Davis tuck him in, say goodnight. 'But I
don't need Mrs Davis, Dad. I need you.' Tonight, as he'd been
getting ready to leave, that's what he'd said, looking at Robert as
though fixing the image of his father in his mind, taking a special
Martin photograph to be filed away somewhere behind those
pale, clear eyes. 'I need you.' And why want to be anywhere else,

do anything else, next to that? The cottage would be warm and light in the darkness of its garden, and now, as he stood in Alistair's hall, it was like Robert could see it. As though he were arriving home at the end of this evening with the light from the window thrown out onto the blackness of the frozen grass... It was where he lived, where his child lived.

Too much. He could feel faint with it, sometimes, Robert could, with the thought of Martin. After four and a half years it hadn't changed, *Who are you? Where have you come from?* As though he couldn't get over the fact even now that the boy hadn't arrived this very night, this minute, while he was standing here thinking about him, delivered to him fresh out of Marianne's body, a son... And what to do with it, that feeling? Certain knowledge of a life that was beginning that hadn't been there before, of time with years in it to grow into, have hopes in and thoughts, plans. What to tell about it, how convey? Here was Marianne now, Martin's mother after all, and it was hard enough to talk about him and he was her child, their child...

Marianne kept his hand in hers.

Her back was to him but there she was, selecting from the

table arranged with all kinds of glasses and bottles, and some barman was lined up behind it, smiling at her like one of her ever-attentive students... *Well, no, I'd never thought of it that way before, but now you make me see...*

'Marianne?'

'What?' She broke away from the barman's gaze, turned around to face him.

'I think we should try to talk –'

'Oh, talk, talk...' She flicked her hair. 'Listen, do anything. You know that with Martin. You never need to check with me.'

'But –'

'But nothing. Be quiet,' she said. 'Now, look, here we are. Champagne, everything. There's a nice man here who will get whatever you want. What do you want, Robert, you poor thing? Why don't I just choose...?'

It was hopeless. Any minute he was going to see someone he knew, or she would, more likely, and that would be it.

'No, don't you choose,' he said.

Any minute. Some friend of hers, some dear, dear *friend*...

'Well then?'

'I'll have white wine.'

But then she said, 'Mmmm, good. I love you,' and squeezed his hand. 'I do, you know,' she said. 'I love you. I love Martin. And I mean it, this can be our conversation about him now, that you're so keen on having. Do anything you want with him, Robert, okay? That's the conversation. Whatever. It'll be fine by me,' and then she was gone. The waiter was handing him a glass and there were people all around him and none of them was Marianne, and the home he'd made for himself after she'd left him, him and Martin, that place deep in the country where no one else lived, seemed like somewhere in a story or a dream, in the back of his mind and far, far away.

'Hi Robert.'

There was a woman's voice behind him, and he turned. It was Elaine, from the paper.

A few more of them were there with her, the same old crowd, but she was the one smiling at him now.

'How are you?' she said.

'Oh,' Robert took a sip of his wine. 'I'm all right...' It was cold, the wine, good. 'You look well, though,' he said, and she did, wearing a kind of a longish dress that made her look taller somehow, more powerful.

'Thanks.' She smiled at him again. 'I haven't seen you for ages…'

'No,' he took another sip, and… Really, why not just leave it? With Marianne? She would always do what she'd done tonight, draw him in, make him think there was some kind of little chance.

'Great party,' said Elaine.

Like that weekend a couple of weeks ago when Martin was away and Marianne had come to see him, just the two of them on their own together, and she'd used the time as a sort of a trap. She would always be up for that sort of thing, always.

'Yeah.'

So try and forget about her — Marianne. Try and never sleep with Marianne again.

'But then, Alistair's got something to really celebrate here,' he said.

With that sentence it was like he had entered the room. The light breaking around him, the sound of so many voices, laughter. All at once Robert felt he'd come into the role of the person who'd been invited, the guest who, more than any other, had a right to be here.

'Cheers!' He lifted his glass to Elaine. They'd come a long way, he and Alistair. 'To Alistair!' Robert said. He finished off his wine, and had the barman refill the glass. Here he was now, in Alistair's lovely dining room, and it was fine enough, really, to be here. He could stay for a bit. For a while, it would be good for him, just to enjoy himself in this bright, warm room... Someone else came up to him, Elaine's friend Jeremy from that magazine, what was it? *Review* something?

'Good that you're here,' he said. 'You never usually come out, do you?' Robert took a sip of wine. 'Not usually,' he said. 'I tend to stay put.'

'In a country cave,' Elaine laughed. 'This must be something for you, Robert, to winkle you out of there.'

'Well,' he said. 'It is...'

'Where do you live?' someone said to him. 'Quite far away?'

'You hide,' said someone else, from Features. Robert recognized her from the weekly meetings. 'What's so special about tonight?' she said.

'Only that it's Alistair,' Robert said. 'I'd come from the back of beyond to put in a show for him. Quite a different thing from you lot.'

They laughed. He laughed. And yes, he could do this. No matter what, he could always do this.

'So you're going to cover it, then?'

'Of course. It's a terrific play.'

'That's great.'

'That *is* great,' said Alistair, coming up behind the rest of them that moment, putting his arms around Robert, giving him the big hug.

'You're the best guest here. Whatever they're saying to you, don't listen to them.'

'We're not saying anything. We all love your play.'

But Alistair wasn't looking at them, he was looking at him, Robert. *You okay?* the look said. It was something they'd had together since they were kids. Robert looked back at him, smiled. 'Oh, I'm not listening to them,' he said.

Alistair seemed happier than he had for a long time. Someone had said there was a new girlfriend, and now, sure enough, he said, 'Beth, Robert,' to a slim, modely-looking woman beside him.

'Robert, yes...' the woman said, Beth. Robert saw her eyes flick, just for a couple of seconds, between him and Alistair, as though she were looking for something in them, in the way they appeared, or how they acted together, that might link them. Then she said, 'I've heard all about you.'

'Beth's in *She Knows*,' Alistair said. He put his arm around her waist. 'She's amazing. I can't wait for you to see her, Robbie...'

'Robbie?' someone said, and laughed.

Quickly Alistair said, 'Seriously. As the mother. She's fantastic.'

'I'm looking forward to seeing it again,' Robert said. 'The whole thing. I mean it's been, how long, since the first — ?'

'Oh, a lifetime,' Alistair said. 'And all the changes. It's practically a whole different play from when you first read it.'

'A whole different play?' Robert said. 'No.' He looked into Alistair's face, those kind, kind eyes. 'It's your play, the same one, from all those years ago. All your hard work. All those other plays in between...'

'And straight into the Court,' said a voice, Elaine again.

'Straight in.' Robert raised his glass. 'Congratulations, Alistair. I mean it. This is the beginning of everything for you.'

Everybody raised their glasses then, said 'Cheers!', 'Hooray, Alistair!' and Robert suddenly felt he could go. Alistair was kissing his girlfriend, his dark head bowed down to her lifted face... It seemed like a good time. He started to edge away. If he left now he'd be back in time for Mrs Davis to be still up so he could pay her and she could leave. Then it would be just him and Martin in the morning. They'd have Sunday breakfast together and there'd be the whole of the empty day ahead and Martin wanting to play him the Mozart, he'd been looking forward to it all week. *Can I now, Dad? Can I? Go for it, Mr Jinty...* And Robert would sit back, watch his son tuck the tiny violin under his chin, look up once, *Ready?*, before he drew the bow down across the strings and began to play...

'Top up?'

A waiter was before him, holding a couple of bottles, 'Red? White?'

Robert shook his head. There before him were Martin's little fingers working their hundreds of fractions across the strings. That dense pattern of quavers and semiquavers you couldn't possibly believe could be managed by a child and yet there it was, that sound, that extraordinary, terrifying Martin sound...

'Sure?'

The waiter was still in front of him. Then there was a voice –

'I don't believe it...' Marianne again. 'You were going to leave, weren't you?'

'Oh, all right then,' Robert said to the waiter, and held out his glass. 'White.'

Marianne put her hand out and rested it on his chest, all her little bracelets running up her arm. 'I got the job in France, you know,' she said. 'Did I tell you? Two years, bit of teaching but mostly it's for all my own gorgeous fabby research...'

'No.'

He put down his glass. He didn't even know why he'd taken it in the first place.

'You didn't tell me.'

'So...' Marianne said then, and she brought her face in close enough to his that for a second he thought she was going to kiss him again, like before. 'I meant what I said, you see. About not putting me into the equation, you and Martin. I'm not going to be around, for a while, anyhow, and by the time I get back he won't even know who I am...' She paused. 'You won't either, Robert.'

He looked at her, that face, that mouth he'd thought just now was going to form a kiss she would place on his skin...

'So just enjoy...' Marianne was saying, 'Oh, I don't know. This —' She waved her hand around the room, the people in the room. 'Everybody here. There's so much more than... me. Your son —'

'*Our* son, you mean,' he said.

'No.' Marianne drew back, slowly shook her head. 'No, Robert,' she said. 'He's yours, little Martin, you know it. Magical, mysterious little boy. He's all, all yours.'

Then Robert turned away. Fully. From her. From everything about her, her mouth, her hair. The dress she was wearing with the back torn off, the arms with their bright bracelets of glass that were around him now, wanting to hold him, comfort him, 'Please...' She was a horror show, Marianne. That was the kind of show she was. The way she'd held that coat of his in her arms like it was the only thing in the world she cared about, her long legs and those bracelets running up and down her arms like water... Just horror, horror...

'No!' He wrenched off her arms and... Damn, but he could feel the sting of them, damn bloody tears, he couldn't believe it. He drained off his glass, another waiter was there and he refilled it, and she was saying, 'Please, don't make me feel bad, you always knew. We've been over and over this, I said it to you when he was born...' And then he finished that glass, too, set it down.

'Shhh...' Robert said then. He put his fingers up to his lips.

'Robbie...'

'Don't call me that,' he said, and he walked away.

He needed just to get his coat and leave. He started down the hall to where he thought the bedroom was but that room was full of people and up ahead was the kitchen which was empty, so Robert decided to go in there instead. Just for a minute, take a breather, have a glass of water. *Do whatever you like, Robert.* Well, from now on, he would. This would be the end of it, he was decided. Of ever thinking he might go anywhere else for help or care, the end of ever looking for something from Marianne, that she could help him, talk of the future, of Martin... His message on her machine should have been about that. That he'd realized, Robert had, that he didn't need her or a teacher or anyone... *Do whatever you want, Robert. I told you that.*

'You're in a world of your own,' said a voice at his back. 'What are you doing out here all by yourself?'

Robert shook his head. 'I don't know. What are you? This is your big night. You should be in there with all your fans...'

'You're my only fan,' Alistair said, coming up beside him. 'Anyhow, I mean it. What's up, you look awful. Worse than usual, I mean...'

'You handsome bastard,' Robert said, and they both laughed – but then Alistair put his arm around him and said, 'Tell me,' and for a crazy, terrible minute Robert thought that the thing was going to happen from all those years ago, when they were kids, at that ghastly place they were both sent to and Robert opening his mouth and that sound coming out, he couldn't stop it, and Alistair being there to help him, always to help him.

But instead Robert said, 'It's Martin.'

And Alistair said, 'Again.'

'And Marianne —'

'Again.' Alistair sighed. 'Listen, don't think about her, please don't. She's never had any interest in Martin, you know that.'

'Yeah, I do know… But…'

'She's his mother.'

'Yeah.'

'Yeah.'

And Robert put his head on Alistair's shoulder, and really it was like they were kids again at school, the same feeling exactly of being safe now that Alistair was here, of being protected and knowing that nothing could go wrong, not really, even though you were a child and you had no power and your mother and your father weren't coming back to fetch you, they weren't going to, already they were far away.

'It's been so long since I saw Martin,' Alistair said then. 'What are the changes?'

'Only… That he gets better. Onto the fifth school by now and they say there's no one good enough there to teach him. Apparently… There's somewhere up north —'

Alistair pulled back.

'Christ! That's a serious thing. I know of that school.'

'They said —'

'It's unbelievable, that place, I mean... You'll never see him again...'

'They said... They don't know what else to do with him. No one does.'

'Like in the play.'

'Like in the play.'

'She knows —'

'Except I don't know. I'm not his mother. I don't know what it means, like she knows in your play what it means... To give a child up that way...'

'But those children were abandoned, Robbie. In the play, what the mother does... That's a completely different thing... To what you're talking about here, this decision... A school, after all —'

'But you said it: I'll never see him again. The music will take him. Actually, I can see that already, the way he's so caught up with it, the way he is... It's like an illness, is how it feels, that he's sick with it, this bloody... "gift" of his... And I can't take care of him, not really, I can't give him what he needs to get well...'

The kitchen door was open, strange on this winter night, in this cold, but it was open and Alistair led Robert there because Robert was crying now, really crying, not like before, trying to hold in the tears, this was weeping, with all of it, Marianne, Alistair, his coat in some other room and freezing cold with the door wide open into the night.

'Ah...' Alistair was saying, gently, over and over. 'Robbie, Robbie...' and Robert shivered, it was the weather, the cold, but it was also the moment in Alistair's play when the lead character says to his brother, 'Every little single thing about you she knows, our mother. She's like God that way. She can come into your soul.' As though the whole act of watching the play, reading it, was become now like Robert himself was taking part, actually, in the play, and the cast, the play itself had been like some kind of a premonition, all of it peeling back to reveal... him, Robert. Alone in his own cold garden at night, the light on in his son's bedroom but the child... somehow not there. And Robert looking on in the dark at the lit window, the only reminder they'd lived there together at all.

'It'll be okay,' Alistair said. 'Really, believe me, it'll work out okay, I know it will...'

Robert nodded, dumb. The tears were finished, the moon shone down. Behind him, and behind Alistair, in the house the party was still there, continuing, for Alistair, for the success of his play, and everybody was congratulating Alistair on the play and Robert would write about it, it would all be there in his column on Tuesday.

'You know what I'm saying,' Alistair said. 'What we've always known, Robbie. That people manage, in the end, you'll come through this. You know it. You've proved it.'

Robert was silent. Proved... But proved what? That he could be left alone? Be only there like the man in the play is left alone on the stage at the end, after his brother has made that speech about their past, and does not walk off, but waits until the lights come up and the audience start clapping? Is that what it was? Because if that was all, it was not enough. Was it? To just survive, just live, with no expectation of love or care or connection. It's being nothing, that's what that kind of aloneness is. With nothing to add to or take away from. Of course it's not going to be enough.

A cheer broke out from inside the house.

'You okay?'

Then the music came on again, all at once in the middle of a track, the volume turned way up.

Robert shook his head.

'You know I wrote you saying all that stuff,' Alistair said. 'In Act Three. It's you telling me there's no one there to take care of us. It's not the other way around...'

Robert looked at him.

'What?'

Then he let out a laugh. 'It's just that...' he said. 'I've just been thinking about the play, just now in my head, I —'

'Listen, I'm serious.' Alistair wasn't smiling. 'All of it. I mean it, how I wrote it, what I said there, your honesty with yourself, it's your strength. You've always known what it is to exist in the world, Robbie. To *exist*, you know, to be fully, consciously alone that way. I relied on you, all the way through, for that. When we were kids, but later, too...'

Robert shook his head. 'No...'

'It's true...' Alistair's voice was very quiet but Robert could hear it, despite the music, all the sounds of the party in the background. 'You weep,' Alistair said, 'but you think that makes you weak? You're like a rock with all its sides bared open to the sea. You've always been like that, had that... obviousness... of emotion, and it's strong, you know, to be vulnerable that way. Your boy feels it. You send him away and don't see him, he's still going to feel it, Robbie. That you're... *present*. Absolutely. It's who you are.'

The music stopped, there was the sound of jeering. Then it came on again louder than before and everybody yelled out, 'Hooray!'

'Well...' Robert looked down.

'It's been a bit of a night, hasn't it?'

'And now the dancing's started...'

Alistair said, 'You should go.'

'I can't believe,' Robert said, 'that's me, when you're the one –'

'Believe it,' Alistair said. 'The whole play, everything... It comes from you.' He took up Robert's hand, kissed it.

'Well...' Robert smiled a little. 'It really has been quite a night. I don't know what to say. Thanks.'

'It's me thanking you, remember.'

'Yeah, well. Whatever.'

'Whatever.'

'The review comes out in the first edition, don't forget. On Tuesday.'

'How could I forget?'

'Okay, then. So —'

'Goodbye, I suppose.'

'Yeah. Goodbye.'

Robert turned, walked back the way he had come, through the kitchen, down the crowded hall. The sound of James Brown was everywhere through the flat, speakers in every room blaring out with the bass turned up too high, *Papa don't take no mess...* Robert opened the door, stepped out without his coat into the cold night.

Despite the noise, though, that he'd just walked through, that he could still hear, actually, out there in the street, reverberating in the still air, in his ears, the boom-boom of the bass, there was a kind of a silence, too, that maintained as he walked down the street to where his car was parked on the corner. It held, the stillness, while he opened the door and got inside, put the key in the ignition — and then there was something else. Martin. The concerto Martin would be playing for him tomorrow morning, the tape Robert had made at the boy's last lesson, playing now in all its force and power and volume as though it were a living thing, made of water and of air, like tumbling down stairs and falling from great heights, from mountains, the music, filling up the car and never bound to the thin metallic strip, not bound at all.

20

Pamela's Tree
A Birthday Poem

Leaves are falling down around us here, they're falling
down, and earth, it deepens too, is how it seems, holds hard
into itself with frost, and any sky we get to see, well, quickly it
collects, slates over, turns to rain and underfoot muds form —

but look! Just over there I see it's summer still and fresh
and green and grass grows and those small flowers
from renaissance books... Oh My! (and there's a word I think — and
maybe wrongly, please correct me if that's so — a word your mother

did come out with sometimes, 'My!' Did she? In such a way?
Quite breathless and wide-eyed, 'Oh My!' Like worlds could stop,
like God Himself had been found out or Shakespeare come to toss his quill
or Manet chuck his brush into the bin... 'Oh My!' that way she had,

to be so deep in and engaged with some new thought, that 'My!'
Oh my dear *Pamela*! Oh My!) But I digress... Because... You see, it's
true, I see that now it's not cold, no, not after all, it's light
this sweet green place where you are standing... You! You've

done it, somehow, pulled it off, this trick, you've made this transformation,
made of all the mud and sluice a spring... A tree... Is what you're like,
a dainty stalk all broken into blossom, tree, of course that's who you
are in this broad springtime of our palest pinks and scented wholly with

the season... Spring! It's spring, not summer, no, not yet. Not that fierce
season with its heats as I thought back there in verse two... No,
Pamela, it's new, this season that we're in, my God it's new, and
we don't have the language yet for what you're going through, but

just for now say 'fresh' the air feels, and how warm the sun and
there's the bump and hum of some poor anxious bee against
your lovely petals, and this spring... Oh Pamela (Oh My!) it's you
I see, like in Japan in cherry blossom time and families,

whole families, they come to seat themselves beneath your
branches... My own first daughter wraps her arms completely round

your waist — 'Can I go in?' she said to me that day when you
arrived in Edinburgh off some flight, and you were sleeping in your

room, 'Can I go in?' and then your voice: 'Oh yes, come in!
And also is that Millie? Millie, I have got some things here
you might like, like look, this cream it's for your feet and would
you like some?'... So, you know... Just all of this, it's

all to say... Say, what? Just love, I guess, more love... For, for sure,
that's what my daughter said to me, the minute she came out your room,
'I love her, Mum, that friend of yours, who's come to us, to here, from
another world, and what's her name again?'

'It's Pamela,' I said. 'Yes, Pamela... It's her,' she smiled, it's you,
my friend, my springtime tree all loaded with her blossom, you...
We sit, say prayers, drink tea, and all the spring is with us while we do...
Oh Pamela. The green and pink when sky may darken, bloom against the blue...

It's You!

21

Roman Sandals

'Hey, chicken, dig the sandals!' is something I could have heard, coming out of the red lipstick mouth of, say, one glamorous auntie. Or, how about a New York mood, kind of? One cool kid yelling, 'Where d'you get those, just gimme those, will ya!' and making a grab for your Romans right then and there. Or there's always, 'I'm craz-eee about these things,' some supermodel or other telling you like it's a secret, and look, now here comes the sun-bleached biker-boy straight out of your dreams. 'These things come in my size, little girl?' he says, taking off his reflector shades and looking just at you. 'Let me have them, honey. Just let me unstrap them from your pretty little foot and see if these babies fit me…'

So, yeah. Fantasies, okay. Because your mum knew damn fine none of that kind of groovy nonsense was going to happen when you had your Roman sandals on. Buckled firmly about the ankles, sensible shade of brown... That took care of the summer and nothing fancy about it. Pair of shorts, stripy cotton dress — you were *sorted*, young lady, and don't even think about wearing jandals if you're going to be doing anything other than moping around at home. Jandals, she said, mothers said, could be dangerous to wear (No running or jumping in those jandals! remember!) and, more importantly, were dreadful for your posture. 'I'm just admiring you two girls standing there with your lovely slim ankles in your Roman sandals,' my Granny said once to my sister and me, marking a high point (possibly the only one?) in the compliment record of childhood. 'Your stance is...' she said, and here she took a short, dramatic intake of breath, 'impeccable.'

The fact is, you have to take a good hard look at the whole Roman sandal thing that was going on in a sixties and seventies childhood and realize the mums had a point. We stood up straight and we played *hard*, we Roman sandals kids. Sure, there were cer-

tain dweebs who wore Romans with socks, white socks, and —
shock, horror — there were some fathers even who got around in
this look. Mind you, with shorts, Crimplene was involved... But
on the whole, though we didn't feel particularly ON in the sandals
(the idea of, let's face it, twiddling them in a biker's lap is, quite
brutally, never going to come off, love), nevertheless the sheer
sturdiness of the footwear combined with its open toe/heel aspect
gave us access to the wide open spaces of adventure and fun
where, mothers are right, jandals were *not* going to take you.

'Let's get our Romies on!' was the clarion call of my cousin,
Alexandra, a gorgeously serious older companion in play.
Alexandra spoke French, played the cello and read really thick
books with tiny print — yet here, with a pair of Romans on, she
would be leading elaborate expeditions across rocks and into the
deepest bush. 'Romies Rangers' was the full name given to our
footwear those long-ago weekends. And nothing could stop us
then.

I think I may need a new pair now. I've still got stuff to do. I
was at a beach last weekend in Scotland and could have used a
pair of sturdy sandals. Actually, I would have chosen them to be

in brown. Furthermore, I think I need a pair each for my daughters, too, one red, one blue. And reader, they would wear them, these little girls of mine... Though it's true I went through a big bare-feet phase back in the late seventies that's with me still, and a legacy I want to pass on to my two-and-a-half- and five-year-old children, slipping a bit of buckle and strap in there too might not be such a bad thing. Because the kids in London have no clue, really, about what a sandal is capable of. And we three could show them a thing or two, I'm sure, down the Portobello Road. I could, you know, *phase them in*. Start popping them into people's wardrobes. A pair here, a pair there. Wear them to key parties, twin them with some Marni, I don't know, extend... I'm in the middle of writing a short story about three little boys who never wear shoes, but I might just write them into the sandals, too. Give them different colours. Make it into a chapter, maybe. Man! Just start talking about those babies, okay? Go up to some biker. At the very least, get my husband a pair. 'Hey, darling!' He turns, and there I am, our daughters are... There the world is... Standing behind us. And look at our feet. 'Everyone, see? We're all Roman now!'

22

Words in Translation

Tatua

I've
plaited myself, often enough,
with paper or with grass or
strips of wool all woven through
to make a shape of mat or bag. I've
formed and shaped a
thing with way more strength
than little bits of thread or string.
But
in the end and more than that
it was just a plait of silk I
dreamed for, heavy as a golden rope

lain down my neck, my hair in such a way
my mother might have done it, yes,
when I was small, and taken time. A
plait, a bow to pinch it at the end. Her twine.

Ngaio

Look — this ghastly arm of dark
and sleekish wood — who does it
belong to? Is it yours? Come off
some woman? Torn somewhere from her
immense and thready root?
It's raining here and cold
in this dark place where I have found you.

Mataatua

All the handsome boys from school
rode up front, and crowded there
at the prow of that long canoe. I
remember how we watched them. At night,

we slow-danced with them too. Their hair
was damp; we pressed ourselves
dreaming against their dark jackets like
butterflies in our thin dresses, caught.

Moko

Blood, ink, the knife
— nothing's changing.
All these things I have,
I am, I need.

Tangiwai

Don't come down with me,
later maybe, if
there's sun or when a high
wind lifts the hills… But not today.
Today it's only rain filled up my clothes
and formed thick muds and sluice of stones around
the graves, the place my grandmother

has lain untended all these years. *Aue*...
My mother, mother's mother...
My wet earth, *Aue*, my rain.

Kainga

Let all of me be a house where I can live.
Let there be doors, rooms to move about in,
open windows... Let the children and the lovers in
— let there be space here for all of us. Hours
of stairs and beds and lamps lit at night,
flowers in jars, bread on wooden boards...
Let me be that house.

23

Domesticity:
Stories at Bedtime

Brush your teeth
and have a pee.
Hop into a bed
and we'll have a story.

The goodnight story has all the comforting ritual of the simplest
of poems. No matter how busy the day has been, how filled with
noise or troubles or excitement, now the children are in their
pyjamas, tucked up in bed, and here we are in this soft, lamp-lit
room, the open book on my knee.

It can feel a bit like magic — the way this beautiful sense of
order is conjured out of chaos. And magic too, because, as I sit
here reading familiar stories it could almost be as though I never

left my own child's bedroom, that I am still there. I look down at my daughters' upturned faces as my mother looked down upon my face as I read and the feelings are the same now as then: comfort, security, pleasure. In the bringing up of our children, when so much is change and alteration and variety, here is one aspect of childhood, of parenting, that doesn't change. The story at bedtime is fixed. It's that last thing we do for our children at each day's end: we read them a story.

As I go back now, with my daughters, to the world of books I first entered with my mother as a child, I realize how resilient those bedtime stories of the past are. For just as my mind was taken up with them then, so now am I fully absorbed by the power of these narratives, the way they are so enmeshed with my sense of self. Of course, all rereading contains a degree of this familiarity: Who we were when we first read a book informs, in part, the story in front of us, it becomes knit into the page. So when we pick the book up again, years later, of course there's a bit of ourselves left there from before. But with children's books, it's as though we encounter our child self whole when we return. They work a bit like myth in that way: as though no intervening years have come between us and the story, no other versions of our adult self to get in the way.

That's different from other rereadings. For example, when I first read *The Leopard*, the voice of the Count was that of an old man and I felt I had little in common with him. His thoughts, his cynicism, his great swell of feeling and melancholy… These seemed way beyond my sensibility — while the story of the young lovers was like the most beautifully wrapped and sweetest chocolate in the box. Then, when I went I back in my late twenties or early thirties to the book, all I saw was the writing — Lampedusa's quiet dramas utterly subsumed by the words themselves. In my most recent reading though… I became the Count. His story came back to me, and that great age that I'd deferred to once I now saw, as it were, from the other end of the page. His world was now my world. 'Everything must change,' he says, 'in order that everything can stay the same.'

That sentiment follows me to my daughters' lamp-lit bedroom. For though returning to a favourite children's book does not offer up the multiple perspectives we gain, as I did with *The Leopard*, in our adult reading, nevertheless when we read to our children we meet ourselves as child and adult, both. Not only am I opening up again those first books that stored up in my imagination all that time ago, but, because I am simultaneously sharing them with my own children, I am releasing the essence of them, as it were, in double strength. Then I see how, though everything has changed and I am far away, geographically and emotionally, from my child's bedroom of the past, yet how close I am to it, too.

This makes reading to children a shared reading experience like no other. The books I loved as a child were of a particular period, I see now, or they had a particular period feel to them — because they came from my own mother's sense of what made a book special. They were 'old-fashioned' in the way they radiated a particular, very British, kind of world. J. M. Barrie, C. S. Lewis, E. E. Nesbit and Frances Hodgson Burnett... These writers peopled my mother's sensibility when she was small, and so that in turn came to govern my own. Even writers I discovered for myself, who set their stories at a later time — my favourites were Rumer Godden and Helen Clare — called upon that same Edwardian world to draw their boundaries, to set the tone.

A. A. Milne and Robert Louis Stevenson worked the same magic in verse… What these writers did was create a world that was safe, ordered and bounded by endless rules and constrictions — in order that the imagination could take flight.

Establishing that dichotomy, setting a closed domestic world against an irresistible fanciful one, is particular to children's books of the past — but has had enormous influence on the ways many children's stories are told right up to the present day. For the deliciousness is in the difference — between good and bad, safety and danger. Crossing the borderline from rules to irresponsibility couldn't be more fun. All children's books, of course, delight in the moment when the imagination has liftoff, but if the world is established as domesticated, safe and settled, and firmly rooted in home-life, how much more do we feel the escape of make-believe, of magic, of lawlessness. To that extent, that Edwardian world given me by my mother in books, and the values generated by it, is one we're still governed by — in our lamp-lit room at least. Order, tranquillity, the fiery tempests of the imagination subdued ultimately by the domestic arrangements of Nanny and Mother and the nursery… These qualities work in satisfying counterpoint, for the time of our reading at least, in our own busy, disorganized lives.

A poem by A. A. Milne calms me now as it used to calm me long ago:

Little boy kneels at the foot of the bed,
Droops on the little hands little gold head.
Hush! Hush! Whisper who dares!
Christopher Robin is saying his prayers.

Here, the angelic boy/girlishness of the narrator, the vaguely sexist distinction between parental hierarchy and the reference to Nanny that occurs later in the poem, for some even the prayers themselves, these could seem well and truly the outdated remnants of another era. We don't have a nanny, and certainly no one today has the kind of nanny that existed in children's books then, but for all that, for all these differences, on the nights we have this poem together, such is the feeling of contiguity around the poem's edges and our own domestic lives, that those details *could* be details from our own lives. It *was* fun in the bath tonight, as the poem says it was, and we *do* wish, like the poem wishes, that God would bless people like Nanny and make them good. The children are probably wishing it for me! My mother had us memorize some of those A. A. Milne verses when we were small, so I can say them to my children when we're on holiday or I'm settling them down in a strange bedroom... And they work their calming effect then. The poems draw out their own boundaries and we become contained within them – no matter where we are... The Edwardian nursery is fixed that way; it's a very safe place.

Maybe that's why the adventures contained there, in the stories, are so wild. I'm reading *Peter Pan* to my daughters now and what strikes me is the savagery, the sexuality, the dark force at the heart of the book, how unleashed that is, and yet how safe we are, too. The world of Neverland has come out of the nursery after all; it was first imagined there, and Barrie is always reminding us of that as he writes. The walls of the nursery of *Peter Pan* open up and the world of the lost boys is contained within it. So you could say, in fact, there is nothing fixed or certain about the Edwardian world after all, nothing stuffy. Certainly J. M. Barrie writes a weird and wonderful sentence, is utterly postmodern, actually, in his consciousness of story as story and of how we, the readers, may enter the text. Here he is preparing for the end of his tale with Wendy, Michael and John coming home:

> We must now return to that desolate home from which three
> of our characters had taken heartless flight so long ago. It
> seems a shame to have neglected No.14 all this time; and yet
> we may be sure that Mrs Darling does not blame us. If we had
> returned sooner to look with sorrowful sympathy at her, she
> would probably have cried, 'Don't be silly; what do I matter?
> Do go back and keep an eye on the children.'

Moreover, while certain aspects of *Peter Pan* may seem dated at first – the obvious gender and class and race issues (mother in charge of dinner and social arrangements, father in charge of the sums at home, the Indians are 'savages' in Neverland) – the domestic scene is actually wildly alternative and avant-garde. The mother tidies up the children's minds at bedtime, getting rid of any awful thoughts; father gets down on all fours and becomes like a dog at the end of the book, going to work in the City each day in a kennel. The Darlings' home is vividly conveyed as a place where rules are extended, values redrawn, roles challenged; and the world underground in Neverland, presided over by Wendy in the end — a woman after all — is not so very different from a modern single-parent household. Safety and freedom… Mothering, motherlessness: these contrasting ideas play off against each other all through *Peter Pan* and make it, for all its Edwardian detail, resoundingly contemporary, full of the same questions, the same uncertainties, that plague us now. My daughters have in their bedroom a window that gives onto the same sickening drop as the Darlings' children's window, four flights up, to the street below. It's left open and trouble flies in: that god of lawlessness, of parties, and of sex, Pan, with his hypnotic pipes saying, follow me, follow me: 'I think,' says Wendy to Peter, before kissing him, 'it is perfectly lovely the way you talk about girls.'

Surely *Peter Pan* prepares girls for boys as thoroughly as one of those paperback teenage novels with photographic covers and titles that hint at all manner of high-school dating dilemmas.

I think it's much sexier, actually. It has a kind of insolence, in the way the writing itself is as ambiguous and open to wild and weird meanings as the world it describes. Almost without our noticing, Barrie slides in huge chunks of morally ambiguous information — Peter not remembering the names of the boys as they fly, being knowingly sly and attractive, knowing and unknowing — happily allowing his story to be sinister and double-edged. There's something of Milton's Satan about his boy's seduction of his little charges and then his neglect of them — and that metaphor of flying is one that both writers use as a way of getting darkness to infiltrate the light. For the mother, for the daughters, there is no one more attractive than Peter. Such preparation for teenage life is there in his tricky, insouciant story.

Rereading him to my children now reminds me of how subversive I felt the book to be as a child — in ways, of course, I could not name then. Now I can see how certain literary devices create these dark effects. Neither narrator nor narrative is to be trusted. The storyteller enters the story directly — like God — to fiddle with it and change it, to be in control, and then to change his mind. So what can we trust when all is moveable?

Who's telling the truth? What is lie, what is the more acceptable make-believe? Is Peter good? We can never really answer these questions in *Peter Pan*. Halfway through and all my eldest daughter can talk about — even though she shivers with fear at the same time — is how handsome Captain Hook is with his black hair and violet-coloured eyes and good manners gone all bad.

The pleasures of returning to a childhood favourite certainly are to do with our adult literary appreciation now built into the sense of pure childish enjoyment in the story. Going back to *The Lion, the Witch and the Wardrobe* recently, I was struck by the satisfying way the story was made, the subtleties of the writing. I don't mean Lewis's renaissance and medieval scholarship at play in the story, or his Christian allegory working itself out within the plot — although these are certainly interesting enough to the adult returning to a childhood favourite. No, what I delighted in more than anything was the particular voice he employs, and the way he aligns the story to the telling of it. That voice, I now see, has always to a large part *been* the story for me — that gentle interrogatively shaped tone that comes from a particular upbringing and education and extends an idea naturally and organically without ever appearing to instruct: 'And now of course you want to know what had happened to Edmund. He had eaten his share of the dinner, but he hadn't really enjoyed it because he was thinking all the time about Turkish Delight — and there's nothing that spoils the taste of good ordinary food half so much as the memory of bad magic food.' It's a North-Oxford-sherry-by-the-fire kind of voice and wonderful to be around. I couldn't hear enough of it when I was small — that voice that loves books.

And words. Legendary *New Yorker* editor E. B. White wrote *Charlotte's Web*, and coming back to that story, too, has the dual satisfactions of re-entering a vividly remembered world (spider's web writing in the corner of the pig-stall, the gentle grey and clever nature of that nimble and sophisticated, even somewhat WASP-ish, spider) and fresh appreciation of the clean, straightforward prose White championed in his magazine: 'Wilbur never forgot Charlotte. Although he loved her children and grandchildren dearly, none of the new spiders ever quite took her place in his heart. She was in a class by herself. It is not often that someone comes along who is a true friend and a good writer. Charlotte was both.'

Children's books stay with us the same way. Appreciation of the words now only shows us in more detail why we loved the story then. When a newspaper asked me recently to describe the first book that had changed my life, the answer came back immediately: Rumer Godden's *Miss Happiness and Miss Flower*. This story, about two little Japanese dolls that come in the post to live in London and be understood by a child who is herself an outsider there, rang bells for me at seven that still sound loudly in my mind:

'Where are we now?' asked Miss Flower. 'Is it *another* country?'

'I think it is' said Miss Happiness.

'It's strange and cold. I can feel it through the box,' said Miss Flower, and she cried, 'No one will understand us or know what we want. Oh, no one will ever understand us again!'

This book is about finding ways of being understood. It's about privacy and society, about the difficulty of making your wishes known. It's about finding a way of being at home. *Miss Happiness and Miss Flower* is structured around the making of a Japanese doll's house (there are even plans for making one yourself at the back of the book) in order that the dolls can be safe, in their own house, ordered and calm. It's like a microcosm of our ideal world, the doll's house, like an image of the child's calm room at bedtime, safe and warm and happy – and Rumer Godden was aware of the importance of those things more than most. Her best children's books happen around and in doll's houses. She, like me, was a writer who did not have a clear sense of where home was, so she made homes for herself in these stories. Reading them now, these books still give me that home. And my own children can come home to them, too.

When I read these books first, had them read to me, I had not been to or lived in any of the places where they were set. Where I lived it didn't snow at Christmas, there were no squirrels or robin redbreasts, but instead there were tuis and cabbage trees and opossums. Much is made now of every country having its own children's literature, of every class, every culture, having its own indigenous sense of itself that way, but when I was growing up the homogenized world of the Edwardian story predominated. How glad I am, though, that it did. For it has allowed a childhood that stretches right back in time: the line goes back from my daughters to me to my mother, and it goes forwards from me to my daughters and their children to come... One lamp-lit room after another.

Hop into bed and I'll tell you a story... The child hearing the stories is the same — though she may be grown up now and hearing them as she reads to her own daughters, discovering the imaginative place within that the story itself first discovered and named and created as a place to return to again and again... This is the joy of reading to children at bedtime. The making of, to paraphrase John Donne, 'this one little room an everywhere' .

24
Ship Song

His gaze was there from the beginning,
swaddled in your arms in muslin wraps,
Sashimi on the grass, the leaves in pale green
patterns on his face as you looked down
upon him and could barely speak, his eyes fixed
then upon your eyes... And clear the gaze again

for Millie when he looked at her and long
that first time, like his thoughts played out
upon her: Well, my cousin, eh? I see, just look
at you, you're lovely, so he seemed to say, what
will you come to mean to me, I wonder, for... I'm
half in love with you? It's true, that look of his, the

look I mean. Clear and grave but full up, too, as if
half sickened on itself, it seems at times, like drugged
with sweetness sucked from all that he has seen...
It's in his songs, also, when he begins some
lengthy thing — about a Gollum stranded from the
light in Tolkien's *Ring* or starts the groovy tune

from our dear unforgotten over-resurrected Lord,
when he sets off 'At last' and 'all too well' when
he has 'seen where we all soon shall be' — the way his
clear, still eyes behold the words complete and held all
in a piece within his mind. 'My God!' That look! It
falls upon us absolute, looking with no thought or

judgement, looking just to see: Just who are you?
his eyes say, and: What do you mean? That I am
safe? He holds this vision still — then seconds break,
a friend kicks in, or someone speaks, or there's a
sweet he wants to eat — whatever, it is gone. And
we must look more closely at him now to see it

for ourselves, that look — for as the days pass life
gives ever-different faces to our children, gives
them different eyes and mouths, they change
the more they wear… But this, this frank,
untroubled stare that still is present,
still is there, reminds me that your son is so a captain

of his life, with seas and ships from two tall men within
in him, both those grandfathers of his who steer him through
the waves, has learned already of the cold and waters that
come down and blind you, learned that seas mean anything
can change… The ice is in him from the north that way,
like red is in his golden hair, it's Viking, sure enough,

the course he steers alone in winds and looking out
to distance… From two unnavigated parents left
behind was this small ship of yours all formed — yet
he will sail just as he will, he'll look ahead, he sees
way more than we do, doesn't need us waving, even,
with that gaze to steer him, doesn't need us calling

'Safe, safe passage to you, little boy' from shore.

25

Now I can see how it was, I think

The McKays came in most weekends, or that's how it seemed anyhow, and always smelling of blood. Everyone knew they killed their animals. Uncle Neil, but the boys too, he taught them how to do it, then they'd all walk in through Gran's kitchen door Saturday morning, smiling the big white smiles like they had knives in them and carrying in their arms their parcels of meat.

'A beast...' That's what Uncle Neil called it, the thing that they were bringing in. Not cow, or sheep, or deer, only, 'I've got a beast for you here...' like it had never been alive on the farm, a creature with eyelashes and breath, but was altogether different and now it was dead.

'Hey.'

That was Davey. He was the eldest, and kind of like a man. He never used to say 'Hello', just 'Hey', like that, while he chewed gum. 'Pull in, will you, so I can get past...'

He'd come in behind me, so close, kicking the back of the chair where I was sitting and hoisting the newspaper lump he was carrying up onto his shoulders. 'Move in, I said.'

The second of his talking was gone before I could even think of anything to say. Gran might ask him a question, she might flip up the corner of the newspaper to look inside. 'What you got there, Davey? Forequarter?' but he didn't even answer her sometimes. Or he said, 'Side,' to Gran, like that, just one word for a reply, or it could be 'Haunch' or 'Shoulder', who knows? None of them spoke much. Just 'home-kill': that was McKay talk, their own language, like 'beast'. 'You want me to butcher that side further?' 'You want me to take a saw to that leg?' It seemed as though the rest of the world didn't exist when they were around but everything had to be to do with hammering or saws or knives. As though everything about them in the end rested in those hefty, bloodied parcels that they carried into Gran's kitchen, piece after piece, to unwrap and rebag and label, lay down end to end in her freezer and try to kill the smell, the smell of more than skin that always hung around the McKays, a reminder, that odour, of who they were, and the kinds of things they did.

So Davey, sure, but they were all like that, three of them plus Uncle Neil — three boys, I mean, but they all seemed grown through and much older than boys Elisabeth and I knew, though Davey was younger than me and my sister, and William and Christopher just kids, still, who would have guessed it? They were skinny and tall, with long hair straggling down their backs, and burned dark by the sun, from being outside all the time, I guess, and Aunty Clare not bothering to call them in. Going past those mornings, through to the laundry where Gran kept her freezer, a big one like a coffin and twice as cold, she said. They would sort things out in there, and Elisabeth and I were supposed to just finish our breakfast while they did it, eat the little triangles of toast, put the jam spoon back in the dish.

'You boys okay?' Gran called out, but of course they didn't answer, and then Uncle Neil would come out and he smiled the big smile again.

'Get the pan on, honey...' he said.

That was the routine, the way they'd come in and offload, then Uncle Neil liked to cook up something from the animal they'd just brought in. There was the smell the cooking gave off, in that sunny kitchen of my grandmother's, and she hated it, because of the mess they made; she complained about it, but Uncle Neil would just come up beside her and kiss her, snake his hand a bit up her skirt.

'C'mon...' he'd say to her. '*C'mon...*'

I don't know what was going on there. Our Gran showed her teeth like an old wolf at him when he did that, she would turn around and whip him hard with a metal spoon or dishrag, but she was often laughing too. And Uncle Neil, well, nothing would scare him. He'd hold out pieces of the liver or heart he was going to fry for us to look at while they were still raw.

'Not much of him left now, girls, eh? That old beastie, but we'll eat him up, anyhow. What you say?'

He kept his hand there with the red on it and I could smell its blood smell and Uncle Neil's breath.

'What you doing, Dad?' said Christopher, when he came out of the laundry, and the others, Davey and William, behind him.

'Just showing our little town girls something from the country...'

'Yeah?'

'Yeah.'

Davey kept chewing gum. The others smiled.

For our uncle it was like an act he went through, this kind of talk, as though he had something to flaunt in front of us and we had no way of coming back, no words. There really was nothing my sister and I could do that might make any sense to him. He put on a voice for us, sometimes, when he arrived, like we were supposed to understand it as a joke and find it funny, something about us being the little girls from town, and asking how was our daddy, don't you know, 'the professor'? 'Do give your father my *kindest* regards...' He wouldn't have talked that way to anybody else. Our father wasn't there to hear it for himself, once or twice maybe, but mostly he drove us up there to Gran's at the beginning of summer and he might stay one night, but the McKays and my father together is not an image I hold a lot of in my mind. So, it was Uncle Neil saying to me and my sister instead, 'How was it, *gels*, in...' and he pronounced 'town' this way, '*tine*'?

It was because of our father, he said, to show respect. 'Don't we, boys? Have to show some respect here, though the professor isn't with us?' But the boys just stood around, they weren't even listening to him. Davey grinned maybe, his face dark and bony and strong-looking, just chewing that gum.

So Elisabeth and I were the children there, made to feel that way anyhow. Just dumb town girls, our own enlarged hearts with the McKays around the only certain thing about us, like the way we felt the whole world was full of boys when they were there, of men. Of their smell, and the darkness of their skins, that hair they pushed back out of their eyes... They were our cousins, but something else because of where they lived: 'farm boys'. Sometimes I used to say those words to myself, in my mind, before I went to sleep, saw the boys take shape around the words, those old T-shirts of theirs ripped through, their dark, capable hands, the way they would twist their fingers into their mouths to make the high shrill whistle that would bring back dogs and horses from the hills. *Farm boys...*

Hard to believe our mother had been their mother's sister. That's what I thought back then, hard to believe there could be any connection. Aunty Clare had married entirely in, become 'farm' herself and so entirely McKay by now it could have been as though she'd never had any other family. She let Uncle Neil grab her whenever he wanted and kiss her in that hungry way — she didn't mind. And she had a new baby and another one growing inside her. She arrived with the rest of them those mornings, but coming later through the kitchen door, her stomach sticking out and the baby balanced on her hip like an extra bag of shopping. The bra strap might be coming down off her shoulder and the skirt of her dress riding up, and she just flopped down on one of Gran's chairs and stretched out her legs before her. 'Make me a cup of tea, will you, Mum, I'm exhausted. Hi girls, want to hold the baby?'

I remember she wore red lipstick, though, and I guess there was a bit of her there, in the lipstick, that I could see might be like my mother still.

'No, no. They were different,' Gran said, when I asked her about the two of them. 'It suits Clare, but that life never would have been right for Charlotte. You can see that, can't you?' she said. 'You can see it in her room.'

You could see it. My mother's bedroom Gran kept just the same as when she'd been a young girl still living at home with her, and my sister and I spent a lot of time in that place. It had a fragrance to it, a kind of sealed-off reminder, like a chamber in a fairy tale where something had been alive once, a princess, but now she was somewhere else and sleeping. Might she come back? There was a little dressing table, glass jars for creams all laid out upon it like our mother might just walk in and sit down before the mirror, start brushing her hair in that long, quiet way. That's how it would have been, I can imagine. That she would have kept herself in front of her mirror with the creams, preparing for the moment when she would step out-side again to do whatever it was she was going to do out there. It was the kind of mirror you could turn out or in so you could see the back of your head in it and I bet my mother used to turn it that way, too, when she was a girl: look in the mirror and see from the back how she might appear later, to someone who would come up behind her and see for himself how exposed it was, that bare and empty part at the back of her neck...

Oh yeah.

That's what Uncle Neil said.

Your mother was something else, all right.

Until I got that part figured, though, my sister and I only had little bits of detail, like the things in our mother's room, to go on — bits of memories, and maybe we were making them up, too: the dances and the clever university lectures with our dad... making up all that stuff about her out of the room Gran kept with the hairbrush and face-powder compact laid out and the silky underwear in drawers. Because, really, in the end, who knew who she was? We were kept apart, Elisabeth and I, outside the possibility of knowledge, the way adults hate to think children might be living in the same world as their own. Though we took the baby sometimes, put him down to crawl around on the floor... Though we lived whole summers in our grandmother's house... We were the girls: 'the two girls'. It's what I could have named this story. And we stayed being 'the two girls' for quite a while, the boys still pushing past us those Saturday mornings, going straight out into the garden after they'd eaten, when they were done with the meat.

More and more, though, Elisabeth and I wanted to be in the coolness of our mother's room. It was the beginning, I suppose, of how things changed. There was the perfume, powder that we could dust behind our ears... It felt safe, with its quiet and shade, like the kind of place where my sister and I could believe we might gather up, in the scent and silken underwear, a power like our mother had found there, that maybe later we could go out into the world of men and use. Aunty Clare got worse at not letting us be there. She'd never liked the idea of our mother's bedroom. Gran said that she wasn't allowed to go in there, not Aunty Clare, not any of the McKays, but still Aunty Clare would come looking for us after we'd put the baby down. 'You girls in here again? Get out, it's not healthy!' Throwing open the door. 'Come on, now! Outside!' Calling through the open window, 'Davey! Be a sport, honey! The little girls want to come outside and play with you!'

No one wanted to play, of course — we were all of us growing up, and for my part it scared me how much I wanted to watch Davey when his mother forced us to be together this way. Watching him from the corner of the garden where Elisabeth and

I sat in our little huddle by the roses, this boy who wasn't even twelve yet, but seemed to have all knowledge in him; it reached down to a part of me I hadn't even known was there. Aunty Clare would have shooed Elisabeth and I outside like we were chickens and foolish, with our cotton dresses on and our knickers underneath, and he'd be just laid out there on the grass in the sun, his long skinny body of a boy, or he'd get up to stretch, reach up to the branch of the apple tree and hang from it:

'What you girls want to play then? Eh? What game?'

It worked for a time, then, as his mother wanted: Davey and Christopher coming up with things to do, and though Davey seemed bored with us already, still we went through the motions of children playing. Walking along the tops of the cattle fences over the road from Gran's house, that was one game, and they were high, those fences, and you could fall. Or they'd make us go running across the highway at the end of town, counting five first when you saw a lorry and then out onto the road and you had to cross it before you got killed. Yet, though in those games I tried harder and harder to be first, to be fastest, nothing either Elisabeth or I did made any difference, in the game, or outside it, to make the McKays like us or Davey notice me, want to talk to me. He'd just stand there, maybe with the others, with Christopher and William or on his own, chewing that wad of gum of his, and I was the one who wanted to be inside his mouth with his tongue and his white teeth, to be right inside and for him to let me stay.

So... like mother, like daughter, I suppose; and though I was forced to go and my mother may have chosen it for both of us, we were closing behind us a door that kept behind it the mirror, the wardrobe and the neatly made bed. In the end, we both wanted the same thing, the same kind of people. It was the scent of my mother's powder, after all, I was wearing, and though the paleness in the bright sunshine of my sister and I next to our cousin's dark is an image from the past, from me, it's also from my mother's life. I see it now, how it rises up again here in my grandmother's garden.

The day Aunty Clare called Elisabeth and me 'the two girls' for the last time was one of these same mornings I've been writing about — Elisabeth and I in our mother's room, at the dressing table, and Aunty Clare came in and made us leave, and outside the McKays were over by the fruit trees. Again I felt that brutal thing of the closeness of the boys, after being somewhere separate and protected, the closeness of Davey standing there, but then he said to me that day, 'Hello,' when he saw me. 'Look what I've got…'

It was the first time he'd ever done that, spoken to me that way, not a 'Hey' or a kick. He had something in his hand.

'Come over here,' he said, and then he smiled.

I saw it was alive, the thing he was holding, a little cat, the stray who lived under Gran's house we called Alice, and sometimes Gran let us feed her and let her come inside.

'I want you to help me with something,' Davey said to me.

The other boys were looking on, grinning. 'Go on…' they were saying to him.

'Get on with it. Just get on with it.'

'What?' I said. I took a step towards him.

'Don't,' came Elisabeth's voice behind me. The McKays did this, after all, all the time, had these animals that were half tame, like Alice, like pets almost, but then they finished with them just the same.

'I know,' I said to Elisabeth, but still I took another step towards Davey. He was still looking at me, wasn't he? He was still smiling?

'You going to come over here,' he said, 'or what?'

Elisabeth said again, 'Don't, Susan,' but I said to her, 'What? What's wrong?' I remember the grass, bright green, around us, and this feeling of a thing in my body and my body couldn't contain it. Bang, bang. My heart.

'Nothing's wrong,' Davey said. 'Just come over, Susan,' and I did, I walked towards him.

He had a string round Alice's neck, I saw when I got close. He was holding her by the legs and she was scratching him and biting him but he didn't even notice. He closed his other hand over her face, crouched down.

'Listen…' he said to me.

I squatted down beside him.

'I want you to help me decide, okay? Because animals like this are no use to anyone, they don't do anything, just get diseases and the mange. So we have to work out, see? What we're going to do. How we're going to do it.'

His face was right next to mine, there was the close tangle of his hair. I didn't know what to say. Sometimes I had patted the cat, in the past when she was inside, or had had something to eat, but she was wild and terrified now and Davey's face was next to mine, his arm was touching my arm.

'I don't know,' I said.

'You scared?' He leaned in, breathed the words into my ear. *You scared?*

'We kill cats like this on the farm, all the time.'

I looked at him and Alice twisting in his hands, this boy made of dark skin and hard bone and muscle. I could feel him right there, his whole body, and the texture of his breath – does that make sense? – was all around me, his presence, those words in my ear, and I put both my hands on his arms then, and I closed my fingers tight as I could around his arms.

'Shit!' he said. 'What are you – ?' and the little cat went crazy, she struggled, raked him up the leg and drew a thick line of blood. Then Davey went to lick it but I got him first, opened my mouth and found his mouth, I slid myself right in. I pushed my tongue in deeper and deeper, until he opened up wide enough to let me and then it was like I couldn't stop, I couldn't.

I had blood on me, from him, when I was done.

It was the scratch on his leg, smeared everywhere. Maybe I should have licked it clean — but I was finished with him by then. I pushed his hair back from his face, and blood was on his face too, from me, where I'd been on him, it was on his neck, his arms... I helped him sit up. The little cat was still there. Davey must have released her but the string around her neck had caught against a bit of the tree and she was caught, half strangled trying to get away. I reached over and unthreaded the piece that was tied up and she shot off under the house, the string still attached.

Elisabeth was there beside me then.

'Look,' she said, and pointed.

I turned, and there at the kitchen window was Uncle Neil.

'He's been watching you,' Elisabeth said.

'What have the girls been doing?' Uncle Neil said when we all got inside. His naked back was to us, at the kitchen bench, and his arms were messy with something he'd been chopping, lying along the draining board in pieces.

'Just nothing,' I said.

He put down the knife and turned around.

'I've been watching nothing then,' he said.

I looked right back at him, at those blue eyes, blue as ever in his dark face.

'I saw what you did to my poor boy...' he said, and his blue eyes went slowly down and then up again the length of my body. 'Whee-ew...' He gave a long, low whistle.

Then Aunty Clare came in.

'What's going on here?' she said.

It was like everything was gone still, like a painting, vivid, the boys standing there at the window, Elisabeth by the bench. My dress was torn, from the cat scratching, and there were smears of red from Davey's blood but I felt very still myself, in the painting, like my colours were done very bright.

'Well, I don't know,' Uncle Neil said. 'But you should have seen her, honey. What she did to little Davey here.' He was talking to Aunty Clare, but not taking his eyes off me. 'I mean,' he said. 'Just look at her. Look at her.'

'Oh, shut up, Neil.' Aunty Clare turned away.

'But what she did. To our little boy. It's got me thinking, maybe, you know, your gorgeous big sister didn't drive herself into that wall after all…' He touched my shoulder with the tip of his finger. 'Maybe…' he said. 'Because seeing my girl here… Why, it's like…'

Aunty Clare wasn't saying a thing.

'It's like she's still here, sweetheart. Your gorgeous big sister. Going to come out now from that room where you've been playing…?'

And, 'Oh yeah,' he said to me then. 'Your mother was something else, all right.'

Aunty Clare said very quietly, 'You're a jerk, Neil McKay!' but I don't think he even heard her. He just kept on talking to me and it was all about my mother, and I didn't look away, I looked right back at him as he went on and on. The boys were still hunched over by the window in a little pack, and my sister was beside me, Uncle Neil telling me all this stuff about our mother, and Aunty Clare just standing there I suppose, because what else was she going to do…? And looking back, you know, at all of this… Now I can see how it was, I think. It's taken me long enough, but writing it down I understand it, I think: that they'd needed to keep us at a distance, my sister and me, in order to keep us all safe. Because none of us had any choice. We were family, despite everything we all did to make each other feel otherwise. Elisabeth and I were related to these people who swore and showed their teeth and used their hands the way they did... And it must have been just as strange for them, having us around. In the end, no choice for them either, and all because of our mother. The one who'd left. Left first that scented room, these people who still lived here, then left her husband too, her children... Left all of us so in the end all we had left somehow, of her, was in each other.

'It doesn't matter,' I said to Uncle Neil.

'Doesn't matter?' he said. 'What do you mean, it doesn't matter? Course it matters, sweetheart. Just remember it was you who got me started...'

'I didn't do a thing.'

'Ah, come on, honey. Come *on*...'

'Stop it the pair of you,' Gran said, coming in.

I can't remember what happened then. Elisabeth and I, we

just walked out of that room where they all were and went off somewhere – Elisabeth's idea – I don't remember where. Hours seemed to pass, a whole long day in itself, though it wouldn't have been that long, and when we came back to the house they'd gone, it was quiet. Elisabeth never said anything about what had happened with me, how I'd been with Davey on the grass; she never said another word. We went and looked under the house to see if we could see Alice and she was there, and we coaxed her to come back out. Carefully, I cut the thread from around her neck that was so tight and we brought her inside. We put her on the bed in our room and stroked her and settled her but when we stood up, my sister and I, to go, she ran out of the open window and back under the house to that dark place where she'd come from, where she'd been born, I guess, and where she would stay.

26

Not to Go Up

(MILLIE)

Not say, 'Okay.'
Why not? 'I'll go to you.
I'll pick you up, I will, into
my arms and take you
from that bed that you're
unhappy to be lying in...'
Why not go up? Just
get you out of there,
the sheets and cover
we made up before...
So what? Let's pull
them from you now,
why not? And have you

next to me instead,
my arms your bed,
old me and not some
duvet, me, I'll take
the lovely length of you…

For you, just look
at you, you're not a baby
any more and I can't hold you
like I did before, your legs
all draping to the floor,
one arm hung down, the other
heavy round my neck…

Of course, go up.
She's nearly six,
this daughter who
has woken from
a dream and calling
for you now
that she'd be held — for

some frail seconds in
the dark she offers
up her fears and she
will tell you
now her thoughts,
but time ticks on
and not much
longer's left and
then — then what?
You'd still not go up?
Still you'd not?

Because you'd
rather stay? In this
small bright-lit room
that now
contains you?
And there's
music there, perhaps,
and books and

friends… You'd be
there with them? While
the time runs out
for mothers and the time
that you have now
is all the time you've got?
You think you have
much longer
for this talk?
You've not.

The baby just this second's
turned into a man, as you
should know — as Mary in white marble
shows — we've no time left to
contemplate the space between the swaddling,
star and manger and the cross…

She's woken up,
it's simple, you
should go

and take her
like you took her
once before
when she was born,
before another
thought
was held inside my head.
I took her then
when I would only want
that she would have
her way:
'Okay.'
Just watch.
I'll gather in
the twisted shape

that's tangled
in the sheets,
nativity and passion
all in one to have

against my breast.
For soon the sculpture,
poem and the rest
will be all that I'll
have left
of you:
in churches
and in galleries,
reminders of this
soft, soft time
of holding,
of the nights when
you did call for me and I'd
go up.

27

Tender

While waiting for her sister to be born,
those afternoon-time nappings with her mother
(who
slowed down
the words
of any
story
she was
reading,
it was
Husherbye
or *Mr Bear*)
the daughter,

this small girl,

would stroke the mother's face as gently

as a two-year-old

might stroke a woman's face

to soothe a child.

'Oh, Little Mummy...' she said then,

'My Little Mummy,

look at you...'

28

Invitation to a Dance

It's time to come back into
this old world, it's time
to step back from the doorway
of that room where light was
bright (for wasn't it? In there before?
And lilies were laid out and more? Full roses
too, and ribbon, sure, in yards, why not, say
ribbon by the score...?) and shut the door.

There now. So that is done.
But maybe you still
stand there and at that broad front
you wait awhile? For what? For it to open

inwards once again, to press against the memory
of light and flowers
just to let you in?
That's what you want?

Oh, rather not. Please cease the thought
of useless trying of the lock. The door is shut
and you did that, it clicked, it closed,
you don't come back, don't make return
in some old frock to that hot place to spin and
on your own be turned... It's time
to come back into this old world wherein the dancer holds
against the heart this dearest thought:

that there's another dance instead,
with quite another kind of light that changes,
grey to morning, lunch to tea,
each second felt: yes *this* and also *this* is me.
Each beat a tiny weight that's felt as real. And okay,
so it's not so bright, and you feel the tiredness
in your feet, or sudden lift of mood (or not) *this*

moment now... It is enough! A different
step of time – turn off
that other light! Be faithful to the way the world
gives up its stuff, in fragments. Like the turning
leaves, say, or the way the foam breaks at the shore,
or dew on grass or – I don't know, but it is nothing
like what went on then, before, what hummed
and thrummed behind that door...
Remember, you have shut the door.

Remember that tonight. Your daughter
caught your hand, the same quick second that
she turned away from you and said:
'You'll never know how much I love you, Mum.'
And whether what she did was true or felt or simply
taken from some song like Kylie when she sings along,
it's possible from words to take a chance, to find in moments
such as these the rhythm of another dance...

A movement of the feet and mind
that's vivid but is not a whirl,

but rather some small way of learning
where to place your shoes upon the polished floor...
A dance that's more like walking, it might be, or stopping,
resting, stilled from motion altogether... All at peace.
A dance that moves in stasis, listens,
waits, finds rhythm in this new old world that's old —

it's time now for this dance.
Fashioned not from bright-lit rooms
or tulle, but is of something — I don't know yet
what it is, but stepped from years or weeks or months
ago: the girls turned into women and the spinning stopped,
began the moment when I shut the door
and found a dance so different from
the dance I made before.

29

Letter to My Sister

Merran…

I know we've talked about this already but thought I would get it down in words, formally, somehow, as a kind of record of (and maybe one day they will read this and have it as a sort of document of our bewildering and complicated and amazing love for them) what we feel for them, our children.

Oh, Merran, our children.

Remember that day, of course you do, when we walked back into the consulting rooms to get the diagnosis of your biopsy and I said to you, as we gripped each other's hands and terrors and the past were rising and hardening frighteningly in our hearts, 'Think about our children…'? And that's what we did. Our children rose up before us and saved us then: Jamie, first born, little Viking for the Gunns with his red hair and dad; then Millie (you bought the pack of pink sleepsuits), our girl; our mother's namesake, Katherine, coming in behind, all blue-eyed, trailing Highland skies... So we took them with us in our minds into that ghastly room and heard the news. I remember we said to ourselves: 'Only think about the children' — like a prayer-paper pasted to my heart is how it felt, for I could have no belief or hope or faith but only that. *Look who's here* was written on the paper, *in here with us, in this ward of cancer, operations and fear... Look who we have made...*

And it worked, didn't it? As we walked out into that 'Discussion Room' or whatever they called it, with its bra shapes and stuffed-breast swimsuit brochures and the rest of it... We focussed on it, hard, kept saying it, repeating it, like pilgrims who had walked the walk... *The children*. Beside any biopsy or poems, divorces or novel, or your new paintings, or some dream of life running alongside the L. K. Bennett shoes, the lunches, the champagne, our childhood, loves and friendships and more... That's what we had, their lives that day and how the thought of it strengthened...

But then. The bulk of timetable kicked in, and life, the simple practicalities of time, and something, in me, anyway, just forgot how I'd felt that day, in the Banbury Hospital: that actually the cancer could come and blast away to death you and me both, Merran, come to that... And it wouldn't have counted for anything. Not next to the reality of our children. Death had lost its sting — all that. We raised ourselves above the heft of our own flesh that day because we had them, after all, we had *them*. Yes, I did forget. And then, yesterday, I remembered...

I remembered because I saw Jamie and Millie walking hand in hand down your garden.

(And at this point now I realize entirely I want them to have this, this letter: I want Jamie to read it one day, and Millie. And Katherine, you must have this letter, too — even though the next bit has the others in it — you must know it stands for you too, darling; ask Daddy anytime to tell the story of you. Aunty Merran calling from the phone box in Oxfordshire to me in the hospital in Edinburgh — the story of your delicious, landed-salmon, more-than-we-could-wish-for presence in this world... Miss Rae! Get Jamie to tell you how proud he was to be able to say he had a 'baby cousin' and also to use the word 'relatives', plural, 'relations', in a sentence about his family... What follows doesn't leave you out, just sets you up: the one who body-surfs across the backs of all the complications, Little Peach, how you do show us all a thing or two, you youngest of the lot, we are all of us totally in AWE of you.)

I remembered what was lodged in me but by then half forgotten... Remembered because it came to me as an image, fixed, like a painting or like flower-arranging: the image of our son and daughter walking hand in hand down your garden... It startled me. Like churches and mosaics and choirs and gold can startle the frail self to thoughts of being all undone... And what was it, Merran, that made it, suddenly and with great power, come back to me, then tell me something new?

Only seeing them as themselves.

And we can't use them. We can't call them up, from cancer wards, from in the midst of our lives, just to say, 'Live! Live! Please live for us!' They're apart from us. Jamie and Millie, Katherine Rae... That's what's in their hand in hand. Their separateness. Their own-ness. That's what came together,

Merran, for us in the golden late afternoon moment of our see-ing... *Think about our children*. Really? Jamie and Millie, they hold each other's hands and that's not you or me — it's only them. They step out into the garden themselves, as though from out of the air. And something in that thought had its beginnings in what went on that day in the cancer ward that did seem to save us... That it's not the fact of them, *our children*, that redeems us, but rather, simply this: the thought that *we're their parents*. That we've been allowed that way. To stand by and bear witness, say no words at all but simply stand and watch as Jamie and as Millie hand in hand come down, and Katherine running through, come down the garden.

Coming through.

30

The Dream Bird

In the dream the bird
is high and flying over sands
that are red dry,
the bird full-weighted
with the sense
of just itself, like all itself
is all the contents of its heart
— and yet
the bird's aloft
and soaring in its flight
towards a mountain. That
is steep and sharp and red too, in
itself too high, is really, for this bird, for me

who's looking at this bird, too high... As now
the bird alights, takes shelter from
the blank hot wind that blows
around it and below, between
two stones it rests,
the bird,
for thirst
cracks water with its beak
from bones. For water
bones, the bird;
alone and from flight stopped
but not rested.

31

Book Review:
Rules of Detachment

There's a movement afoot in contemporary literature that tends towards stasis. The last couple of years has introduced us to American writers like George Saunders and Jonathan Letham, and, on this side of the Atlantic, D. B. C. Pierre and, most recently, Harriet Vyner — all of whom practise the art of an imaginatively constructed literature that moves us forward in the story while maintaining a kind of withheld emotion, an emotionlessness, if you like, that halts psychological development. We are no more intimate with the characters' inner lives, their moral selves, at the end of the story than we were at the beginning.

Yet, as literature, this new writing is also richly rewarding and satisfying. And a new novel, *The Best People in the World* by Justin

Tussing, is a perfect example: written with insight and imagination that make every page seem to shine, bringing words and their meanings and metaphors into brilliant, startling relief. Tussing shares with Pierre an extraordinary facility for language, a generosity and quirkiness and imaginative overflow… Both of them have words to burn.

The Best People… tells the story of seventeen-year-old Thomas, a sweet kid who runs off with his high-school teacher, a sexy, thrillingly insouciant twenty-something who has him in her thrall: 'She looked at me with an intensity that made me sick,' Tussing writes, in his typically appealing way that, within nanoseconds, compresses a range of emotional registers and descriptions that unhinge all our literary expectations and send us off on a new kind of reading. 'Her pea-coloured sweater, her suede boots, the point of her chin, her pale pink gums.' This is love — yet feel, in this book, how different it feels.

With them on their journey is Shiloh, a social misfit and potential anarchist who's handy with his carpenter's tools and can turn his skills from bedheads to bombs. They come upon a derelict farmhouse in Vermont and decide to stay there through a long idyllic summer that slowly, with the inevitable change of season, turns cold on them, makes them start acting just a little bit mean.

A lot happens in this book — but a lot doesn't, too. Deep themes are hinted at: fertility versus barrenness, the social versus the individual. There's a commune that the three friends dally at, there's an adopted child they play happy families with then give back. There's a shadow pregnancy, a mysterious explosion in the basement, a sense of Shiloh's dark past... All seem to give the story thrust and onward motion but actually come to nothing in terms of plot. The real interest of this book is the making of a home — or, to put it more precisely, as Edward Said did when describing the act of literature, 'the making of a home in words'.

For Tussing writes with endless exuberance about rafters and doorways, bed-frames and kitchens and a well-stocked larder. He writes turbulently and ravishingly about food and bedding, the making of fires, growing of vegetables, the concocting of a squirrel stew. In so many ways, this writing, I think, this joyous celebration of domestic life, is his novel. In words he constructs a place where his three characters can, for a time, coexist — he brings about a narrative that way.

When an early section of this novel first appeared in the prestigious New Fiction issue of the *New Yorker*, it recommended itself as being a story that didn't need an extraordinary turn of events to hang itself on: the words, the construction, were enough. Here's Thomas with his mother before he's about to run away from home: 'I was in the kitchen watching Mary debone a chicken. She slid the blade under the skin, making quick, jabbing cuts. I liked, suddenly, to be near her when she did simple tasks. I was full of sentiment and affection. When the phone rang Mary indicated it with the greasy point of the knife.' *Au point*, indeed, this little paragraph — the boy about-to-be-a-man still at his mother's side. There's his dreamy introspection, her deft dissection, the casual indication of the knife... Much more is packed into this scrap of text than you might think.

The Best People... book stands out from its fellows in this way. For those other contemporary writers — led from the fore, I suppose, by Dave Eggars with his 'A heartbreaking work of staggering genius' — all, at the end of the day, have pretty sensational stories to tell. They may downplay this in their writing style, but their plots full of parentless children, ghosts and murders, and cartoon characters for protagonists... this is the stuff of high drama, using big, self-conscious, look-at-me emotions for its impact.

Tussing is different. He makes us care about little, near-invisible things. We get all bent out of shape when he describes a snowfield or a crow on the end of a string. What we don't get, as we don't get from any of this new writing, is that tug and pull into a character's heart.

That's ultimately the problem for me with all this disaffection. For there have always been writers standing aside paring their fingernails while the story unfolds, and Hemingway and Brett Easton Ellis and James Kelman and the rest can all do a fine job of seeming not to care. The difference is, their characters draw us closer and closer to them in spite of the narrative stance. Their writerly detachment becomes a way of having us emotionally engage. This is how stories get placed at the central parts of our lives — when words on a page lead us onwards and outwards and inwards. This other movement — well, it's more like a wonderful dance.

32

At the Acupuncturist

Katherine ran straight in,
sat on his chair
and swung her legs and said
(when he asked:
do you know
why you're here?)

'To stop my cough and my
sore throat... To take away
the dreams that I don't like,
to give me
more awake-
ness in the morn-

ing's what I want' — and (yes,
I paraphrase), he told me, Gerad,
all of this. 'Your daughter,
she's a trip,'
he said,
'Amazing

and she's
all in
blue, she's
water, energy,

she's...

life!'

33

Delphiniums

All I see
(at this point, Christine)
when I see you
(and I see you,
Christine, right now
all
the time)
is this:
you standing,
skinny, glam
as hell
in Lesley's
kitchen, New Year's

Eve, the year,
this year, two
thousand years
and five...
And you
are wearing
(all I see
you dressed in
through these days
is this grey)... wow,
a dress?
What dress? It's more
like
Azzedeine Alaia,
early nineties, kinda,
painted on the body,
baby, is more like
this groovy
cocktail number
you've got on,

you

pale thin Russian,

with your eyes the

colour of delphiniums,

your eyes, that

shade of blue...

This

all I see

of you.

The rest?

Forget it,

hospitals

and stuff, and tubes

and wounds and

bloody ugly gowns

and awful from-the-kitchens-

of-St-Mary's food...

Forget

the lot,

just all

of it… For we
(your friends
who stand
about you now, to
wave you off, and
kiss you for last
times and hear
your great, great
voice and hold it
in our hearts) see
none of that, but
only
all the images
of you
that fix,
stay printed…
These,
Christine,
just these
are you.

Like, for me,
it was you
in that dress
that night you
wore, your
luscious
laugh
when I proposed that
Lesley, you and me
slip up the stairs...
Us hanging
in
the bedroom then
and having fun, all
times like that,
the times
we saw
and
loved,
delighted in,

your clever
sideways smile,
your groovy Queensy
smoking
talk,
the way
you say
the things
that lodge like
rocks into a stream
into the mind.

Like this:
'Oh God,' you said,
(a while ago, this was,
but feels like you just
said it now)
'When I gave birth to Marilyn,
oh then I knew,
just what the body,

what the female body
could be capable
of doing, to
bring this
child
into the world,
this child…'
You closed your eyes.
'Oh Marilyn,' you
said, you say,
forever, actually, Christine,
for all of us you keep on saying
words that we
remember, that sit
true.
You strong
and straightforward woman,
Christine Koslov,
artist, mother, lover,
friend, in your grey dress and

smiling

with those eyes of yours,

delphinium

forever,

eyes

that

shade exact

of palest

blue.

34

Sisters

The third time coming back down the same piece of road they see it, the turn-off, and take it. All day the rain has been falling. They've been driving all day and this is how it seems, that the rain is part of things, what they see, how much they can see – and maybe that's why they missed the turning before because it's like all they can be used to by now is just that film of water on the windscreen, on the glass.

'I'm sure it was…'

'Yeah, I know. It's smaller though, isn't it, than we remember? And I don't recognize that sign.'

'Everything else, though,' Lara says. 'Look –'

And there's that big tree, and they can remember that, the way it sits hunched like a woman, like a big old lady with her long black arms flapping to them, *Come in, little children, come in*, and all her bark and branches black, the colour of cars to drive to funerals in.

'Yuk,' says Elisabeth and, 'Yuk,' says one of the voices, a little echo, in the back.

So, what was it? Three times they passed and missed it? That's weird, when, okay, it's been a long time but still they know this stretch of road pretty well, they know it. Must be the weather then, making it hard to see. Falling down all around them, the rain, in kind of pieces, like torn scarves hanging down out of the grey sky and wet straight away when they got out into it. Just unbuckle one of the children and open the door and there it was, the wrap of water at your back, so in the time it takes to put one of them into a pushchair to walk across a country road to buy a sandwich they've got to think about changing all their clothes. It feels relentless to Elisabeth in this way, as though she's never known rain like this in her life, this kind of rain, like there are rivers coming down on them now, seas.

Lara said she thought it was tropical, the seasons all over the world different to how they were before.

'Global rain,' she said, when they'd been talking about it in the morning, first thing, before they came out. They'd woken in the motel to the sound of rain on the roof, the Kitten disturbed early by it, before dawn, and the others soon after.

Mum,

Mummy.

Little moans in the dark.

We have to come into your bed.

In a way, that's how it started, the mood established then that the weather would prevail, that they'd begun the day tired, find-ing their way around here after all the years away, with the morning getting lighter but still dark enough that even though it was late summer it could have been a winter morning for them here, with this clouded sky, these wet roads. And this rain, think about it and it does have a kind of sleek quality, like tropical rain, although where they are now is high in the hills, and not tropical these trees, stands of them on bare moorland grass, crackly and skinny, made thin by wind. There are those bunches of them forming woodland up on the ridges, at the edges of cliffs and gullies, like they're huddled together for protection, for dark warmth. That river they passed before is a place that gets frozen over in winter, the rocks cracking black out of great plates of ice, and they can remember skiing, sometimes, on the hills behind the Parsons' farm, where Jim Parson fixed up a tow-rope from the generator in the barn and all the kids could use it.

So, in the end, not tropical.

'It can't be *that* different,' Elisabeth says, 'to how it used to be...'

'Nah!' Lara's chewing gum, likes to do that when she's driving, something she started when the twins were still tiny babies, said it gave her an edge.

'How many years though?' Elisabeth says. 'Since we were last here? How old were we then? Eight? Nine?'

'No time has passed at all,' Lara says. It's a boy thing, talking while you chew.

'Okay, one year,' she says. 'Two, maybe.'

'Is how it feels.'

'Is what I mean.'

The road takes a sudden turn and Lara holds tight to the wheel. She's right, of course. Elisabeth knows what her sister's saying. Because they were just kids when they were last along here, but it may as well have been just the other day, the time between then and now, coming down this road with Gran in Elve's old truck, all those daffodils in the back...

'Remember the —?'

Lara nods. 'They were beautiful.'

They'd picked all of them out of that one field and then just piled them in a great yellow mass upon their father's grave.

'That was just after he died,' Lara says.

'But already it was like he'd been dead forever.'

'Yeah.'

'Yeah.'

Is how it feels.

Is what I mean.

A voice pipes up from the back seat. 'Can we have the nurseries?' she says. 'Can we? Please?'

Elisabeth gives Lara a look: *Do we have to?* They had the tape on all yesterday afternoon and she's only just got the tunes out of her head now. It's all animals and farmyard songs and little creatures of the forest finding their own way home... Without turning around she says to her daughter, 'Let's just be quiet, shall we? Let's notice things instead. Like where we are, don't you think it's spooky?'

'But I want those nursery rhymes,' says Em. 'I do...'

'But look how spooky and great it is here...'

'Oh, let her,' says Lara.

'To sing to you,' says Em. 'I want to sing to you, my lovely mum, and to my lovely boys...'

The twins don't answer. Elisabeth pulls down the mirror flap and sees them sitting there in the reflection, faces impassive.

'Not the tape now,' Elisabeth says to her, then to Lara, 'She'll forget about it.' She turns around in her seat. 'Shall we stop the car, boys? Do you want to get out for a while? Go for a walk?'

They shake their heads. 'It's too cold,' says Davey.

'I love it when it's cold,' says Em.

'See?' says Elisabeth to Lara, and mouths *She's forgotten...*

'And nurseries are good for when it's cold.'

Lara laughs. 'Look darling,' she says. She holds up the tape. 'I'm putting it into the machine — but just wait two minutes, okay? Because it's not far...'

'Okay.'

'How not far?' says one of the boys, John.

'Well…' Elisabeth thinks about it. There was the turn-off five minutes ago, then that stretch of river at spate now down by the side of the road — so yes, they really were very close. In fact, why even ask about a walk just then? You wouldn't want any of the children getting near it, hearing that exciting rush of water. All it would take would be a slip of mud, the bank and… Like that time they watched the old sheep go in, Elve's dog straight after it and both of them in seconds out of sight…

'Remember that day?'

'Remember how they were about it?' Lara replies. 'That was scary…'

'Like don't think about it, it's not such a big deal…'

'That was when Dad was still alive.'

'But Mum had already left.'

'Oh yeah.'

'Oh yeah.'

And then Lara puts on a funny voice 'Dat lady lo-o-o-ng gone, Leetle Girl…'

'What are you two talking about?' says John.

'Nothing.'

'You said it was your mum. You said "Little Girl".'

'Nothing.'

'Tell me.'

'It's just nothing, sweetheart,' Elisabeth says. 'Promise.'

But of course it's not nothing, how can it be? When they're here on this road after all, the same river, the same trees. And, sure, it's the cemetery comes into it, the finality of where they're going: their father's grave, their grandmother's grave, Elve and other people from the village they used to know... But it's also their mother in the story here. And nothing is nothing about her, though they've tried to make it so. Packing bags and booking rental cars, finding maps and places to stay, driving all this way and with each mile, each piece of road, getting closer to the place where she used to be, where she married her husband and had them, her two little girls... Nothing is nothing at all.

'You don't recover from a thing like that,' Lara had said last night. 'Our father can't have recovered. That's why he died, Gran died. Why we were sent away.' They'd finally got the Kitten settled with some milk, the other three asleep in the little bed-room and Lara had brought out some wine. She wanted to talk, so they'd sat there at the motel Formica table and talked and talked. About their mother, that woman they can't even remem-ber, not really, just her scent, her leaning down to kiss them goodbye, but her story somehow all caught up in this story of what they're doing, what they're doing here now.

'We never wanted this any more than she must have wanted it...' Lara had said. 'This place, look at this place. There's noth-ing here, only emptiness. What must it have been like for her? It must have been impossible, after what she'd been used to, like it feels impossible to us now.'

'I'm not sure...' Elisabeth hadn't known what to say. They'd never discussed their mother this way before, imagining her, trying to understand why she did what she did. 'I think so.' Lara kept filling up her glass. 'This place must have been like a trap for her, her husband's family all around, that sense of him being connected. She must have asked herself what she'd done, marrying him, coming here... Then she had us, and it was fixed, that this was where she belonged... That she had to stay...'

'I suppose she must have missed her friends...' Elisabeth had said, but quietly.

'Maybe,' Lara said. 'I think she missed all kinds of things.'

'And we weren't enough for her.'

'We were never enough. If she wanted so much, how could we be?'

It felt dangerous to Elisabeth; it feels dangerous still. Keeping the past separate, that's what they've always done, the sisters, since they were sent away to school, through the years of growing up, growing older... They've kept this place of memories and things forgotten far away. After all, this was their mother they were talking about and now they were mothers themselves, their own children only just gone to sleep. She wanted to say last night but dare not speak out the words: Be careful! Don't come too close! Just keep her as nothing, our mother. Because knowing nothing about her, next to nothing, it's protected her and Lara from the memory of their mother for all these years. Don't start wanting to find out now, who she is, where she ended up. Knowing nothing is a way of staying safe. So when Lara said to Elisabeth last night, 'Whether she's alive, living as an old lady somewhere, or stuck there behind the cemetery gates with a stone at her head...' Elisabeth had silenced her at last. 'To know anything more about her would be too much to know,' she'd said. They must keep the past separate, like they've always done, more than ever before. It's the only way.

And yet...

'Slow down...' Elisabeth says now. She pushes down the button to open the window.

'Smell...'

There's that rich water smell, the river, rain. Dark leaves with wet sluiced through them, wet earth. The whole landscape alive with the past, growing. Seeds coming up through the mud, little trees taking root and you can feel the warm rain giving life to these things, they're here, they've always been here. The smell of growth, of water, comes in. You can think for a while none of it has anything to do with your life, children bathed and hair washed at night, fixing the seven o'clock drinks, putting lipstick on. You can think, you can think: *This. This*, as you drive to work in the morning, drop the girls off with the childminder. You can think: *This*, as you turn to your husband in the dark, wait for him to turn, *This*; but then there's the other moment now, two sisters, and all the damage rising, the memory of how it was for them when they were children, they were little girls and children of their own now with them, the sense of that, it's all around them in the rain and in the vegetal smell of the rain.

And the smell is also beautiful, Elisabeth thinks, she wants to keep it. Because it's the smell of growing, it's why she wants the window open, that reminder, like she might let the water, the little seeds, come in. And the rain is also beautiful, look at it, the beautiful wet slicing down the windscreen as the wipers thwack-thwack, back and forth, across the glass.

'We are nearly there,' says Lara. 'See?' She points out the broken-down old building half hidden by a stand of trees. 'The hanging rack.'

Elisabeth looks at it, only the back of an old shed, but they used to imagine it like gallows, one long plank of splitting wood extending low out of the side, high enough, Elve used to say, with a good rope, to scare them. For a cat, or a horse. Or a man. It would always do the job.

'Jesus,' she says.

'Old Elve.'

'Yeah.'

'What a trip.'

'Who's Elf, Mum?'

'Oh, just an old man we used to know. When we were children...'

'Were you children?' Em says. 'You and Aunty Lara children?'

She and the boys laugh, then start chanting, 'They were children, they were children...'

'We were children like you,' Elisabeth says. 'Once...'

'Upon a time,' says Lara.

'And an old man called Elve looked after us sometimes, with our Granny who was like our mother...'

''Cause your mother was a-dead,' Em says.

'No,' says John. 'They don't know that, do you? Mum?'

'No, we don't know that at all,' says Lara. 'Sit back in your seat, Em.'

Last night John had come into the kitchen, late, Elisabeth has just remembered. They still had the glasses, the bottle on the table and he'd come in, it was while Lara was saying that if they were to actually go into the cemetery, to find out if their mother's marked grave was there, would be the difference between thinking of her as connected to them somehow or another woman altogether. John had been in the room then. 'But why would that be?' Elisabeth had said. 'Even if she's no longer alive, why would she have decided to be buried here? After all the time? It makes no sense.' And Lara had said she didn't know, but it was something to think about, to tell themselves, tell their children, that their mother's story may have ended with her coming back to be buried next to her husband, for her to have come home to them that way. 'That's crazy,' Elisabeth had said, and she'd said something about the children then, about how the children should never know about their mother leaving them the way she did. 'I don't know why we've brought them here,' she remembers now saying to Lara, over and over. 'It's better for all of us that we keep her out of it. We've told the children that this visit is to show them where their grandfather's buried, our grandmother, actually, the cemetery... That's fine. That's all we need to do. We don't even need to go in.' And John must have stood at the doorway and watched them, heard it all. 'It's best not to know. Really. If she's there too,' Elisabeth had said. And that's when she'd said, 'To know anything more about her would be too much to know.' Then they'd both looked up from their talking and their drinking and they'd seen him, the little boy, watching them.

'You don't, do you?' John says to Elisabeth now. 'Mum told you she doesn't know.'

'Well…' Lara says.

'You said there was a stone or she'd be alive.'

'Johnny —' says Elisabeth.

'And grown-ups are supposed to know,' says John.

'Yeah,' says Em. 'They are supposed.'

'So you can't be grown up, then,' says John. He leans forward and pokes Lara's shoulder.

'Can you?'

Lara is hunched tighter over the wheel, peering ahead through the rain and she doesn't answer. They've turned the corner so it's the final stretch and there are more trees, and the bush is starting to thicken around them, and there's a wind.

Suddenly it feels like a lifetime they've been here. Like that old building back there, the piece of wood sticking out, could just reach over and grab them, pick them up, one under each arm.

'I've got you,' Elve would say. 'I've got you safe.'

'Jesus.'

'I know.'

'We should have kept the children out of this,' Elisabeth says.

'I know.'

'What?' says Em.

'Nothing.'

'Bringing the children here, bringing them right in... We shouldn't have...' But they have, haven't they? Brought the children right in? Meaning just to have something to tell them, a nice journey in the car, something to show them about when their mothers were children, but ending up on this road, even so, where the past is buried, over with, it's supposed to be, yet look all around them, the rain, the dark, slick grasses... And how to keep it apart, the past? How to keep themselves safe, and the children? Keep them safe from asking questions the sisters can't answer, because that's what children do, ask, 'Why?' Why did your mother leave you? Ask. Why any of the mothers in the world might leave?

But too late for any of this now, too late, because they're here. They're at the cemetery gate. Lara pulls the car into the little driveway and switches off the engine. 'Listen,' she says.

The wind's gathered, lifting up from the rushing water of the river, passing through the trees. The thin grass stamped down and dried out from the long summer is live now with rain, water running off the low hills either side of the road and the wind chasing it. Like a deep moan is what it's like, coming out of the far trees, over the next hill to be here, round the car, with them.

'It's calling for us,' she says. Like Elve used to say, 'The wind's going to come for you, too, one of these days. Just pick you up, two little girls, like it picked up your mother and carried her away...' And Gran would say, 'Be quiet. Like they need you telling them about any of that...'

'Just carry you away...' Elve said, even so.

And now the wind again, the same wind.

'This is not how it was,' Lara says then. 'It's how it is.'

Elisabeth nods her head, yes. For that's exactly it. The past become the present now, like this journey would always make it so. The car barely able to go forward, so it seems, up the narrow way, but you can't go back either. And the rain has joined the wind by now to make a kind of wailing, *Aieee*, like ghosts in the dark trees calling. Mother. Father.

Aieee... Aieee... Like Elve is there and Gran, all the people from the village who lived once upon a time in this lonely place...

The wind's going to come for you, too, one of these days. Just pick you up, two little girls, like it picked up your mother and carried her away...

Elisabeth turns to see if the children are okay but they're just sitting quietly; it's as if they don't even notice the sound outside the car. Little Em's eyes are closed and she's concentrating on forming words, each syllable framed by her mouth, carefully, slowly...

'Springing is gone
and winter is here,
and what will the robin do then,
poor *thing...*'

Her eyes remain closed, her beautiful, pale grey eyes, but her face, the expression on her brow, shows she is thinking… *Poor thing…* The boys look on at her unblinking, in a kind of dream.

'He'll sit in the
barn…' Em sings quietly.

'Try to keep his self
warm…'

They are all, Elisabeth, Lara, Little Em, the boys, the baby, nearly asleep.

'And hide his self under the
wing,
poor
thing…'

There's a hush, sigh, and Davey, then John, lean back against the seat. The Kitten has settled into her side of the carrier, thumb in her mouth, blanket up around her cheek. Elisabeth turns back and sees there before her the gate, the little path behind that winds up the hill to the graves. Lara is sitting very still, like she's just a little girl. Like all those years ago, to keep herself calm, going absolutely still, like there are wild animals all around them, circling the car, huge animals.

'We shouldn't have come here,' Elisabeth says. 'It was a bad idea, for us, for the children. I know we said we'd do it, bring them to the village, and here to the cemetery to show —'

'Shhh,' Lara says suddenly. 'I'm going in.'

Elisabeth turns. 'What?'

'I won't be long,' Lara says.

'But —'

'Shhh,' Lara says again. She nods her head back towards the babies. 'You'll waken them.' She starts to unbuckle her belt. 'You stay here,' she says.

Elisabeth can't think what to say. 'But —' she starts, Lara's hooking up her buckle.

'We never decided that we'd do that. That we would actually go in —'

'Doesn't matter.'

'We said we'd just come here to show the children. Where our father is, their grandfather —'

'That was a lie.'

'But —'

'Anyhow,' says Lara. 'They're sleeping, you have to stay

here with them. So it's not us going in, you and me. It's just me.'

'But —' Elisabeth has to think quickly. 'You don't need to,' she says. 'I mean, if it's just for the children, to tell them. To prove —'

'It was never for the children,' Lara says.

'But —'

'It never was. You know it. It's only us, Elisabeth, it's only ever been us. All the time, not thinking, about this place, our mother, trying not to think about any of it... It's always only ever been us. The quiet girls, remember? Who don't ask questions? The good little girls who don't say a word? Anyhow...' She opens the car door. 'I want to see the graves. The children are sleeping. It's a good time.'

Elisabeth tries to think of something else to say, to stop her, but Lara's out already in the rain. She smoothes her hair back from her head, looks up into the sky and then walks up to the cemetery gate.

The wind is blowing in through Lara's open door and the rain blown in with it, onto the seat, onto the steering wheel. But

Elisabeth sits there as though she can't move. *Please don't* is what she wanted to say to her sister, just now, what she should have said. *Don't make it be like this.* They should decide together, what they're going to do. They should be always together. They need to talk about it more, don't they? Think about it some more? Last night, well, that was the beginning perhaps... But not all at once, deciding now what to do all at once, they should be together for that, and with the children, too, maybe, who knows? They could figure something else to do. Just because long ago... Just because... That doesn't mean they have to figure everything out now, right now; there are other things in life, in their lives. Like they could wake up the children instead and just go outside, maybe, walk around a while, maybe, make it okay, just a normal thing to do — but it doesn't have to be like this, a big thing, and Lara leaving them behind. She was her little sister, Lara was, she had to look after her, she was the one who stood perfectly still while Elisabeth brushed her hair in the morning, before school.

'You're fine,' Elisabeth used to say to her.

'I know I'm fine. You're fine, too,' Lara used to say back.

So she had to look after Lara now, didn't she, and protect her? And Lara stay close to her, too, look after her, not go away to… Where she's going now, where she wants to go. 'Don't leave us now!' she wants to say, like wanting to say it all her life, 'Don't leave!' Always she's looked after her sister, and her sister has looked after her, always it's been them together, the two little girls, remember, and even now she could call out to her sister, Elisabeth could, 'Lara! Hang on! I'm coming with you.' While all of them are still together she could call out, 'Wait!' Wake the children up out of their deep sleep and, while there's still time, these women and their children still together by the gate… Elisabeth could call out, she could, and go out after her sister, into that world of grass and trees and soaked earth, of the slip-road and the graves, and bring her sister back in.

But she does nothing. And Lara doesn't turn around. The gate is slippery at her fingers, stiff in the wet for lack of use. The high sound of the wind is louder than ever, the rain in the wind more insistent than it was before… Elisabeth leans over and closes Lara's door against it. She turns the engine on once to wind up the windows, switches it off again. Then everything is quiet.

One of the children stirs, one of the boys.

'Shhh,' she says, without turning around, in a low voice. 'Go back to sleep.'

And now Lara has unfixed the gate and it's swinging inwards, and still Elisabeth could do something but she does nothing. Through the flooded glass of the windscreen Elisabeth watches her sister walk away from her up the path, getting smaller and smaller. At the top of the hill, she stops, seems to hesitate for a moment, looking back as though she might be going to wave goodbye, then she turns, disappears over the hill to the part of the cemetery where the graves are, to the part where — and Elisabeth knows this suddenly — their mother is waiting for them.

35

The Sheep and the Lambs

The sheep are crying for the lambs.
It is dark; I did not expect it.

Earlier, this afternoon in yellow light,
the tractor came, the farmer's dog,
and rounded all the sheep together,
put them in a pen beneath the shaded
trees... You'd know the rest.

But no. For I came back into my room
and there I saw across the field
the same red tractor had come back,
the gate was open now and spilling through
the break across the yellow grass, a slow escape

of sheep returning to their home. The sun
was wide across the hills, the hills
were fine, with woods and houses at the
front and heather, mountains all behind.
But then, the sound began at night, the cries.

And when I woke next morning, saw them
standing there along the line — I knew then
what I'd heard: it was the lambs that had been taken.
And the sheep were waiting for them still, the cries
the calls of mothers for their babies,

their spring lambs for slaughter in the autumn
gone from them by now, before their time.

36

Drawings — Fragment

They were three boys and their father had died when they were very young.

It happened this way: Ray had a big yellow stallion that never got tame; some days he said it was good as gold but then others it turned mean, its eyes red and rolling, rearing up on its hind legs and sweating all over. Ray had kept hold of the horse because of its value and because he didn't want to admit he never should have bought it in the first place. Even when it went crazy, crashing through barbed wire fences and tearing itself up, Ray still wanted to think that someday the beast would sweeten and he'd get it out on the racecourse which was why he'd bought it in the first place.

Anyway, that didn't work out because the horse got shot. Ray was saddling it up one day when it suddenly lunged at him, twisting back its head like a snake and then coming down on him, showing its teeth. Ray put his hand up to grab its head and the horse went for him then; he managed to duck but took a savage bite on the arm. He made it back to the house and had his wife, Carolina, drive him to town to get stitched up. Once all the blood was cleared away his arm didn't look so bad; the horse had bitten deep, the doctor said, but it was neat, and should heal up easy. That night, one of Ray's brothers came over to herd the stallion back up behind the pines, where he shot it. Next day was the A & P show and Ray was supposed to be doing the demonstration dog trials there. He said he still felt up to it and that his arm in a sling made no difference. As he raised his fingers to his lips to whistle the dogs into the pen he fell from his mount, haemorrhaged, and was dead in seconds. An A & P show is like a big agricultural and livestock fair. There were a lot of people there knew Ray Burton and his family, saw the whole thing happen. It was a big panic. It turned out from the coroner's report that a clot had formed in Ray's blood after the horse had bitten.

The pressure of it had built up and built up until the blood broke. Nobody could have known it would happen. Jim was just a toddler and didn't remember his father or the day, but Johnnie and David were older. They knew there was something wrong because of the red stuff coming out of their father's eyes and nose and mouth. David knew it was death, the way his father turned into a body, lying in the trampled show paddock and streaked with slippery red. Someone put their hand over his eyes so that he couldn't look any more. After that he stopped thinking about it, is what everyone thought, except in dreams.

The boys were brought up by their mother alone. All this happened, you understand, a long time ago. There had been nothing unusual, in those days, for a young woman who had married young and moved out onto the farm to be with her husband to stay there after his death. Even though Carolina had no relatives or friends living nearby — and after Ray's death stopped going to the nearest town much at all, just to get supplies in when she had to, little things for the boys — still, no one said anything about her moving away, coming back to live some place where people were. The farm was isolated enough, though, down an unsealed clay road that meandered for miles through the hills after the last turn-off from the main road and it was high, into rough land, a lot of it, on the tops with scrub but known generally as good sheep country and no need to sell off any part of it, even with Ray gone. His brothers continued to live there just the same with their wives and families, and at the house where she'd been brought as a bride, Carolina seemed set to stay. Spring went into summer into autumn into winter... And here's this woman alone in a big house way off in the middle of the country, with three young boys under the age of five... How does it seem to you? Reading this now, thinking about it? When so much has changed and our lives are different, how does it seem to me?

As I say, this was a long time ago. I hadn't myself given the story any thought at all for years, how it might have been to be on my own in the way she was, or how it might have been to be brought up the way those small boys were, on their own with no father and just the memory in the eldest of the fall of all that blood... Then I found myself in a gallery in New York a week or two ago, and something of the past began to stir. I was supposed to be meeting a friend in a lunch place downtown, a little place, it's been there for years, but I was early and the friend, I knew, would be late. So I was walking around, looking at shop windows, when suddenly it began to rain and to get out of the weather I ducked into a gallery. It didn't look like a gallery from the street, it didn't look anything more than a doorway, actually, but once inside it was like all those galleries that used to be around that neighbourhood before Prada or Gucci or whatever took over and it gave me a nice feeling, that kind of Spring Street in the old days feeling, when the neighbourhood, the whole city, was like a kind of theatre and you never knew what was going to be on the stage. It was just a big white room, the space, with large drawings pinned up over the walls as though with Sellotape, as though the paper itself was of no value but was the kind children may use at nursery school, and there was a man hunched over a desk in the far corner of the room with another large piece of paper in front of him, part of it on the desk, part falling to the floor. At first I couldn't see what the drawings were, they were in crayon, just thin, thin lines in pale colours, barely outlines at all in places... But then I got closer, and the man in the corner looked up... And it was like everything came in on me then. For the drawings were drawings I knew, like they'd come out of the deepest parts of my dreams, and the man who looked up at me from the desk, the skinny man with his jeans hanging down and his raggedy hair... He was my little cousin, the youngest, the one who'd been no more than a baby when his father was thrown from the horse that day, and went down.

37

Katherine and the Mouse

Katherine said, 'Oh, Mum!
There is a mouse!' or something like,
And I said, 'What?' while she bent down
to look more closely at
the tiny thing
lain down quite near the ankle
on my skin
and that I'd thought
was leaf mould to the touch,
like that, quite damp and cool
(we'd both of us
been bare-feet and in sandals
all that day...)

And she was right,
there was a mouse there, leaf mould
in its colour only — grey. A small
grey mouse upon my foot…
'He's sweet,' said Katherine then,
and went as though
to pick him up but I said, 'No…'
and closed him in
my palm instead — now what to do?
For Katherine knew
right from the start
the mouse was lost

and needed to be put back
in his home — it's what
her eager hands had wanted straight
away to do — and was I wrong to take the
little thing instead of her?
For I said then, 'Why don't we
just now put him in the park?

Across the road? Where he
can be outdoors and fresh?'
And she did not say yes,
but still we went
and crossed the road
and did that,

put him down out there in the
bright sun and then returned…
We got right up
to our front door but
Katherine stopped, she said
she didn't think
the mouse was safe at all,
that he'd be frightened,
in the park, he wouldn't
like it in the light,
she said again
that we should take
him home…

Is what we did.
We ran across the road
and the mouse was
where we'd left him
trembling on a stone.
We took him back with us
again and brought him home.
There is a crack
by our front door,
a mouse's house
– he ran straight in and
Katherine said,
'Goodbye.'

We talk about him often as we pass,
in jackets or in coats, about to step
out in the street,
we linger at the opening
of the door, that corner
of the skirting board…

I feel again the pulse
upon my skin, the scrap
of life, the tiny beat of heart...
The start of those beginnings,
Katherine's own
new life, connected to
all living things.

38

Boys and Bikinis

Just say the word 'bikini' and feel the heat coming on. One of the most revealing pieces of clothing we can wear, the bikini is irrevocably romantic, soaked in memories of summers past and dreams of summers to come. Our hopes for our bodies and our suntans and ourselves are all tied up in those tiny scraps of fabric, held together with hooks and eyes and bits of string.

Sure, a bikini takes up less suitcase space than any other article of clothing, but how it dominates everything else you've got folded there. Because from the moment you dangle it in your hands in a department store prior to trying it on, you begin to feel like the kind of someone who is just out there enough to wear one. Say the words 'My bikini' now. See? Ka-pow! That little outfit of stitched-together triangles is clearly *so* much more than the sum of its parts.

I've been thinking about bikinis a lot recently. I've been writing a story that's set on the beach and though the main character is a fifteen-year-old boy there are a whole lot of teenage girls in there too — lying around on towels, having parties, all of them dressed, pretty much, in bikinis. I wanted to capture that feeling of being fourteen: what it's like when you go to the beach or the pool with your friends and you don't have a boyfriend, or maybe you do but you're not quite sure about him. So you look at boys and they look at you and you feel rich and ripe in your skin, but nervous too, full up of all these private feelings you can't tell. Seems to me it was all about swimsuits then. When we're young and about to enter adulthood, swimsuits, bikinis are often all that's standing between us and sex.

It's a teenage memory, then, the notion of the bikini as a powerful charge, a reminder of the detonated adolescent hormones — proof that we remember all too well how it felt when we first put on those tiny tops and bottoms and went out and showed ourselves to boys. The beach and swimming pool could be seen as a kind of theatre for our developing sexuality to show itself, for us to practise and pose. Yet never did we feel more self-conscious than during those first early years of near-nakedness. That's a feeling that extends to the present. For no matter how much feminism and post-feminism we muster about ourselves, the issues about our changing bodies that are foremost in our minds during adolescence are, for most of us, there in every bikini season throughout our lives: Can we wear a bikini before the diet? After the diet? Before a tan? After the baby? I'm not just talking about the dreaded male gaze, you understand. No. Every summer it's the gimlet look we turn upon ourselves that matters most — and that of other women, our friends, families, daughters.

A recent incident with my seven-year-old daughter is a case in point. It was she who, after I'd donned an Hawaiian-print number (Roxy boy-trunks for bottoms and a seventies top made from two triangles) and was feeling, well, just confident enough to go out onto an Australian beach, said: 'Oh, *Mum*. I really *don't* think you should be wearing that.' With one stroke she made me go to the mirror and look again. Was she right? Now that I was a mother, far away from the teenage girl I'd once been, was my choice of swimsuit a foolish one? Or was I being practical, my bikini a cool option in the blistering Australian heat? I stood there considering. Shallow or sensible? Reliving my youth or being a practical mum? The thing is, I just didn't know. Worse, I suddenly felt like I looked like someone who didn't.

Of course, we're peculiar in Britain about such matters. We get embarrassed easily. We don't live in a country that has guaranteed long, hot summers spent lying around in swimwear. I know many European women, of all ages and body types, who take off their clothes and throw on a bikini without giving it a second thought. 'The stomach is beautiful,' says Claudia, Italian and mother of one. 'Of course, we're no longer young girls who look beautiful in bikinis, but bikinis are beautiful for every woman.' These women have a different *feel* for the bikini, somehow. A French friend tells me: 'My mother took me shopping for my first bikini when I was twelve. It showed I was becoming a woman. Now that I have two children I am that woman. Naturally I wear a bikini now. It's like a sign: this is who I am.'

It's true. Bikinis have always been about a certain kind of show and tell. My daughter instinctively knew that when she spoke up. It's why she didn't want me to wear one. She didn't want her mother, as she so damningly put it, 'acting like... a *teenager*'. 'But then,' says a clever fifteen-year-old I know, 'everyone feels the same about swimsuits. Vulnerable. It's the same thing for boys and their trunks. There's generally, for both sexes, a whole lot more... um, skin, on display.'

In my novel the girls in their tiny swimsuits wield independence and strength in ways that the poor boys can only be dumbstruck by. My German edition is hip to this notion, using, for the cover, an image of bikini-clad girls sunbathing for the camera, their eyes averted, though, to its prurient gaze. A boy called Ward stands with his mate Alex at the water's edge and 'even if it would be easy to turn around and look at those girls because none of them are looking over this way, stretched out on their towels', I write, 'So what? They'll just be talking to each other... words Ward and Alex could never hear, none of the guys could hear, unless they were lying up there with them, they'd have to be that close... "I know what you're thinking," Alex says, he puts his hand on Ward's shoulder. "But don't. There's no

point to it, baby." He laughs a brave, fake laugh. "Those girls…"
he says.' Those girls.

So acting like a teenager might just have a power all of its own.
Playing out the idea, no matter how reservedly British we may
feel, that for a few days each summer we might set aside the cerebral and intellectual parts of ourselves and become our bodies
first. That we might just think: Who cares? I don't give a damn!

Maybe that's why, after years and years of wearing a black one-
piece (I'd been wildly influenced by a *Vogue* summer travel
fashion story in the eighties) I finally wanted to put on a bikini
again. Because, why not? Because, though we change, deep
down we don't change and because the story of our entire adult
woman's life lies with us on our towels at the beach: through
puberty to adulthood, through monthly periods when our bel-
lies swell and flatten, through phases when we diet, when we
don't, conceive babies and bear them. Because, as one strong-
minded friend puts it: 'All these changes are signs of my
amazing, capable body.'

And finally because to reach for a bikini again, after all these
years, is to reach for a piece of clothing that tears you up inside

with memories of burning sun and salt water, tanning oil and desire, giving you back, even if only in your mind, the days when you had nothing else to do but lie on the beach all day and think about boys, boys, boys. Thoughts of a busy working mother about a life gone by when everything was spread out in front of you like a long, hot summer's day, lazy and full with the easy, gorgeous luxury of time.

39

Small Pieces for the Girls

Haiku 4
(MILLIE)

Your arm upon the
pillow like a branch across
a path: don't touch it!

Haiku 5

Katherine lies in
the dark, shock still, eyes open,
whispers sentences

to herself: what she
will and will not do, the names
of children she fears.

40

Car

The car was parked right outside and there was stuff in the car. There were broken books and magazines and clothing, for example, there was make-up in the car. I saw lipsticks and I saw mascara and I saw various creams, some tubes of cream that were squirting out, and it was quite old, the cream, and some of it had smeared all over the little make-up bag that itself was broken-looking, its contents spread out over the back seat along with all the other stuff I saw, and my daughters, my two little girls saw it, they are three and six, and they saw the stuff, too, inside the car, the clothes, the underpants... The car was right there, pulled up in front of our house, right outside like it was parked there, only it wasn't parked there, it was just pulled up and naked-looking somehow, the windows half wound down or open and this broken stuff inside, this half-torn and half-used-up stuff like tights, she'd left her tights strung out along the front seat and they were stretched out, poor things, and raggy and old.

We could see it all. Like that little make-up bag with the bust zip and the dirty cream inside, anyone could look clean inside the car and see it. They could come out with us, out of our front door and they'd see it straight away, think, oh, I don't know, think, Whey-Hey! Hell! or, Jesus Christ! They could think: Oh look 'ere! Look at this 'ere bleedin' car. They could think... What did my daughters think? They could think... Anything. The car was perfectly exposed that way, its interior was exposed. There was no doubt the car... There were tampons in the car... This was a woman's car. There were tampons and they'd been taken out of the box, out of their wrappers even, those cellophane wrappers, they were undone, not used, okay, but split and open, dangling with their little strings, and there were panty-liners in the car, in sachets, in their pastel colours, but panty-liners all the same, and they were sprinkled out across the back seat, too, you know, not opened and not used-up-looking, but spoilt, because of how they'd all been ripped out of the box that had contained them, that small place where they should be now, should have been.

'Look,' I said to my daughters. 'What is this?'

We'd stopped outside the car. We were on our way to school.

'Who has parked here?' I said.

What goes on in one's mind now, in one's head? How interesting this is? This car with all this stuff inside? Does one think a thought like that? Wonder at this stuff here in the car, at all this stuff? And all of it that should have just been tidied clear away, just all of it, not spread out in the way that it was now, the underwear, the blouses and CDs all pulled out of their sleeves, and they'd get spoiled that way, they'd be broken. Is it curiosity, inside one's head, that keeps you there and staring — like getting a sort of artwork, installation, there, right outside your own front door, and you're just on your way to school, you're just about to walk your daughters to their school?

I could have said: Look! What we have here! How interesting this is!

I could have said: This is like an artwork, something like an installation, and right here outside our door!

Instead, I said again: 'Who's parked here?'

And my daughter, my oldest daughter, said, 'I think that she is lost.'

We walked closer towards the car. We saw how broken-open were the windows then, not wound down at all but forced, the window on the driver's side, and the back window had been smashed. There was glass spread along the back shelf of the car, weather had got in. Lighter things, pieces of paper which I saw had writing on them and a bra, these gave the impression of having been blown about inside the car, there was rainwater pooling on part of the floor, and there was stuff outside the car, too, in the gutter, that had blown there.

As I said, the car was parked just outside our house.

I think that she is lost.

Two things happened then. I said: 'We have got to get to school on time.' I said that to my daughters. But almost as I spoke I also knew we had to rescue all the things inside the car. It was my second thought, my bravest. To gather up the things inside the car, to keep them for the woman who had been there, safe.

But I did not. I took my daughters to their school. When I came back, years later, the car was gone.

41

Katherine in a Red Towel

Out of her bath and shiny like a grape,
puts the red towel over her head
and moves in through the door.
'Whooo!'
Are you a ghost?
'No,' says the towel, and she pulls it off.
'I'm Katherine!'

42

The Sea in Literature

When I showed my sister the title of the new book I was working
on, she let out a cry: 'You can't possibly call it that! People will
think you're trying to copy Hemingway!' I looked at my words at
the top of the page. 'But mine's called *The Boy and the Sea*,' I said.
'It's quite different' — and for sure, though Old Papa was something of a ghostly Poseidon striding the waves at my back when
I'd come up with my title, and my book, like his, is short — that
word *novella* comes into it — there'd been no question that my
The Boy and the Sea was meant as any kind of copy, or *hommage*,
even. Still, it started me thinking and my thinking took me
straight to the sea.

For the fact of the matter is, it's not the substitution of 'boy'
for 'old man' that makes the books sound as though they've

been washed up on the same shore. And it's not that, like Hemingway's, my story is chiefly about two characters and both are mentioned in the title. No, it's the word itself does it. Like Mishima's *The Sailor Who Fell from Grace with the Sea*, like Iris Murdoch's *The Sea, The Sea*, like Hemingway's masterpiece — it's as though these titles have a rip tide to them, the word SEA breaking upon our consciousness like a wave and pulling the other words down into it. All we see, all we hear, is the sea.

That promise of mystery and hidden depths, the notion of the unknown, and, more importantly, the *unknowable*, that extends well beyond the bounds of certain storytelling conventions surely challenges the great landlocked tradition of the novel. Even Robinson Crusoe makes small mention of the watery world beyond his horizon of sand and palm trees: the sea may be regarded but is not engaged with. And the great stories that follow — from Tolstoy to Balzac, from Eliot to the Brontës, Thackeray, Dickens and the rest — all these are set down on stable foundations, rooted into earth and paddock, streets and houses. Of that period of great 'big book' writing of the eighteenth and nineteenth centuries, only *Moby-Dick* is awash with the kinds of uncertainties and ambiguities that can't help but present themselves once the sea announces itself as the setting for a story.

Moby-Dick has been described as the first modern novel — and certainly the minute the sea enters literature, literature starts changing. It is the sheer mystery of Melville's subject, whales and water, so different from the drawing rooms and villages of previous novels, that makes it a fit for that looser, more organic style of writing that we think of as being of the twentieth century. Rather than trying to constrain the story within the historically established controls of plot and character interaction and suspense, Melville lets the sea in — and we, readers, feel the hymn of his mighty novel wash over us:

It was a clear steel-blue day. The firmaments of air and sea were hardly separable in that all-pervading azure; only, the pensive air was transparently pure and soft, with a woman's look, and the robust and man-like sea heaved with long, strong, lingering swells, as Samson's chest in his sleep... but to and fro in the deeps, far down in the bottomless blue, rushed mighty leviathans, sword-fish, and sharks; and these were the strong, troubled, murderous thinkings of the masculine sea.

The Jungian idea of the sea of the unconscious, a great collective dream-space that sounds deeply with all of our lost memories and desires, that can be dipped into and dredged for ideas and inspiration, instruction for who we have been and who we are to become — this is the very swell of the modern novel. Writers like Chekhov and Mansfield who created a whole new genre of fiction known as 'slice of life' writing introduce a literature that seems to make itself, as though instinctively and naturally, out of ordinary day-to-day events. In their stories, as in those of Woolf and Hemingway, we simply, without formalities of introduction or set-up, plunge into the subject — more water imagery here — *in medias res*... The empirical gives way to the intuitive, logic to sense.

Even Fitzgerald's *Tender Is the Night*, which sets itself up at the seaside, ends up defining itself by that position. The erratic fate of the Divers in Fitzgerald's novel (it occurs to me to think of their surname now in this certain watery light), the ambivalence and mystery of their lives, is predicated in that novel's opening pages. 'On the pleasant shore of the French Riviera', it begins, then upends any sense of stability or order by presenting the known world as an uncertain, trembling reflection: 'In the early morning the distant image of Cannes, the pink and cream of old fortifications, the purple Alps that bounded Italy, were cast across the water and lay quavering in the ripples and rings sent up by sea-plants through the clear shadows.' The love story begins directly after the two protagonists have 'faced the seascape together momentarily'.

This reminds us that there is a whole encampment of what we might call seaside literature – with stories like Chekhov's 'Lady with Lapdog' that are set in seaside resorts and have water as an accompaniment to social concerns, but also use water emblematically as a way of rising above them. Proust's second volume of 'Remembrance of Things Past', *In the Shadow of Young Girls in Flower*, is a perfect example here. As a boy spends his days and nights at a seaside hotel learning to perfect the manners and sensibility of maturity, it is what goes on beyond the windows and promenades, the shifting planes of the sea, that distract him and make of him more than a man, an artist. He inhabits both the known and the metaphysical world simultaneously: 'On the beach in the foreground, the painter had accustomed the eye to distinguish no clear frontier, no line of demarcation, between the land and the ocean.'

That sense of transcendence, the sea making it possible to rise above and beyond one's normal expectations, limitations, is, of course, a great theme of seafaring novels. How could it not be? We're no longer beside the sea, now, we're on it – and characters become bigger than they were before, more dramatic, more wildly drawn. There's the satanic Captain Ahab in *Moby-Dick*, and the biblically named outsider who is its narrator. Then one can look out also to Stevenson's *Kidnapped* and *Treasure Island* as towards a ship in full sail on the horizon. No discussion of the sea in literature would be complete without reference to the tradition of sea-voyage writing, and there's nothing small or quiet about that genre. More recently it has shown its appeal that way in its easy translation to the screen: films like *Jaws*, *Castaway* and *Master and Commander*, and *A Perfect Storm*, based closely upon Junger's novel of the same name, are all examples of how the sea makes an easy epic of a drama. It's as though simply by showing itself to the camera the sea makes a story more grand in scale, more mysterious and metaphorical. Think of the great blood-soaked wash around Quint's boat in *Jaws*, the murk of the sea at night, the rollicking waves of *A Perfect Storm*. As the critic David Denby remarked of the film *Castaway*, where Tom Hanks is thrown up on a desert island after an enormous shipwreck-style plane crash, 'the sea is the real main character of this film'.

It might seem, then, that just as a book's title might favour that word 'sea', so the sea, simply by being present and active in a novel's theme and construction, cannot help but become its chief subject. In the Booker Prize-winning *Life of Pi*, Martel writes masterfully of a tiger and a young boy aboard the same lifeboat, but he also writes masterfully of the water that surrounds them. Listen to this description of a storm at sea:

> Climbing the giant swells, the boat clung to the sea anchors like a mountain climber to a rope. We would rush up until we reached a snow-white crest in a burst of light and foam and a tipping forward of the lifeboat. The view would be clear for

miles around. But the mountain would shift, and the ground beneath us would start sinking in a most stomach-sickening way. In no time we would be sitting once again at the bottom of a dark valley, different from the last but the same, with thousands of tons of water hovering above us and with only our flimsy lightness to save us.

This quality of *experiencing* the sea, feeling what it is to have it there right next to you, floods and works in contrast to the story's conventional narrative devices: Will the boy get home? What's going to happen next? Even when it is calm, as it is for the main part of the book, it is always out there, active in our imagination even while it is passive. The sea is an omnipresent story that way — something a traditional narrative, serving the dual functions of expectation and resolution, can never be.

So we could say, then, that the sea in books really does create a particular and different kind of reading experience — one where we give up the linear expectations of plot for a kind of in-the-minute pleasure that is less passive and objective. It's more active, existential. No wonder Virginia Woolf called her most avant-garde experimental novel of voices *The Waves*. In that book, characters' sensibilities wash against the page, rhythmically, insistently, resisting the man-made constraints of storyline and beginning—middle—ending architecture of drama and its resolution in favour of something more seamless, naturally expansive and inevitable. A certain kind of sea-soaked narrative insists upon the plot changing its course as with the tide, running adrift, plunging ahead without necessarily having anchor or mooring place… Our reading gaze is not so much cerebral regard as a rapture. We are taken up, mysteriously, wholly… In *The Waves*: 'The sea was indistinguishable from the sky, except that the sea was slightly creased as if a cloth had wrinkles in it. Gradually as the sky whitened… the cloth became barred with thick strokes moving, one after another, beneath the surface, following each other, pursuing each other, perpetually.'

This kind of irrationality, if you like, may be the reason that the Highland stories of the writers Neil Gunn and Alistair McLeod manage the deep sentiment of their themes with not a hint of what we in this country disparagingly call sentimentality. Their tales of simple rural life, of faithful dogs and fishermen and farmers and families become paradigms of enormous moral breadth and gravitas because something more powerful than the human heart is driving the action. Both writers seem to paint their stories with sea water and as a result they have the signature of things beyond our control. McLeod's collection entitled *Islands* is itself a perfect description for his fictional project — stories surrounded by sea, characters, situations defined by, altered by, their relations to the space of water around them. His novel *No Great Mischief*, while nominally about a certain kind of Highland history, is also predicated upon its sense of the sea. The story is centred around a forced sea voyage and a drowning — and all the vulnerability, the isolation of human life comes to be played out in terms of the merciless icy water that surrounded first a small boat of starving emigrants, then took a family down into its depths and kept them there: '…for other than the light there was nothing, and the ice seemed solid right up to the edge of the dark and sloshing void.'

What does the sea mean, then, in books? What are its metaphors? Well, first, there is this most obvious one of danger — the killing sea. There's Alistair McLeod's ferocious ocean, and

Neil Gunn's that he sets his little ships out upon in *The Silver Darlings* and then leaves us to wait, along with the women on the shore, throughout the rest of that book, for the men to come safely home again. There's Iris Murdoch's curious novel with its heady title, where the images of the sea bashing up against the rocks, or lying with a menacing oily calm, are the only images with real meaning or force. 'I looked with amazement upon my familiar swimming places, and on the gentle crafty lapping of the calm sea against the yellow rocks,' Murdoch writes in *The Sea, The Sea*, and she commands our attention this way — 'The sea was shining into the room like an enamelled mirror with its own especial clear light' — though really her story does not deserve it. It's the danger of her sea, its relentless presence against all the prattle of Murdoch's thin, unbelievable game of charades that makes us want to read through to the end. Her sea is dangerous in this way alone: it shows how insubstantial is the rest of her imaginative and literary world.

Then, there is the idea of the sea as existing beyond the edge — of land, of society, culture. Virginia Woolf and Katherine Mansfield, as they did in literary terms, also show the way here.

Writing at a time when feminism was in its earliest stages, when the very notion of a female writing had yet to be described, these women created books that still go against the tide of society. They put women, not men, in the central position in their narratives — and empower them by their idiosyncrasies, their quietly antisocial and rebellious sensibilities. Here's the superb Mrs Ramsay in *To the Lighthouse*, commanding her dinner table and her seaside world: 'It could not last she knew, but at the moment her eyes were so clear that they seemed to go round the table unveiling each of these people, and their thoughts and their feelings, without effort like a light stealing under water so that its ripples and the reeds in it and the minnows balancing themselves, and the sudden silent trout are all lit up hanging, trembling.' All this woman wants, from the beginning — the title says it — is to get out upon the water. To get there, to get to... To resist stasis, convention. The society of women as described in that book and in Mansfield's *At the Bay* is something new in the land of books. It's unworldly, it's *other*. Not only do these female characters have power but they are as like the sea in their unpredictability, their waywardness, as is the writing that describes them: '"Oh, these men!" said she, and she plunged the teapot into the bowl and held it under the water even after it had stopped bubbling, as if it too was a man and drowning was too good for them.' Mansfield's words seem to leap off the page. Like her women, they are unwilling to be restrained.

Which leads, finally, to the metaphor of largeness: the sheer expanse of the sea, the great, generous incomprehensibility of it. There's the calm, gentle, maternal rocking force that can also turn, like the goddess earth mother, devouring and violent, demanding of sacrifice, blood, death. Melville's sea is like this. As is Mishima's, Hemingway's... This sea is where you go to when you can't conclude, when the sea itself is the beginning and the ending, containing and swallowing all meaning, all understanding. It's the Old Testament's 'darkness moving across the face of the waters' sea, a kind of infinity within an abyss.

I wanted my own pages to be drenched in all these notions of sea-ness: of limitlessness, of femaleness – but maleness, too. For what happens to the boys when they go into her, the water? The sea speaking, feeling, having her own story... That was what

I wanted for my story. I wanted her wateriness in my writing. A different kind of writing, therefore? I hope so. In the end the sea can't help but make writing different, the subject becoming the writing, the subject taking over… So in the end, our consciousness is so flooded that we wonder if we understand anything at all. It's just the sea there, like she always was, like she always is. As Elizabeth Bishop writes:

> Because we live at your open mouth, oh Sea,
> With your cold breath blowing warm, your warm breath
>   cold…

> Breathe in. Breathe out. We're so accustomed to those sounds
>   we only hear them in the night.
> Then they come closer

> But you keep your distance.

43

Ceol Mor

My father plays a *pìobaireachd* that I love called 'Lament for the
Children'. A *pìobaireachd* is *Ceol Mor* in Gaelic; it means 'big
music' and is the most solemn and worthy form of composition
for the bagpipes. 'Lament for the Children' was written by the
great seventeenth-century piper McCrimmon for his seven
sons, all of whom were killed by plague – something I cannot
imagine, to lose all the descendants that way, in one season, all
the babies, the children, all the young men gone. Yet here I am
with my two daughters and the only sound I can hear now in this
tune that my father plays is the sound, in seventeen scant sylla-
bles, of my own lament, for our children, David's and my
children, our lament for them.

Last Haiku
(MILLIE AND KATHERINE)

They don't come in now
and our bed is too big and
we are small in it.

44

A Farewell

This will be my last thing. My birthday is still a couple of weeks off, falls on a Sunday this year, and the girls are planning a special supper at home with candles they can help me blow out and a cake with jam inside and cream... We're staying in. How much time has passed in this small year.

A couple of days ago, at breakfast, there was a bit of a spat. Nothing major — and nothing new there, of course: breakfasts on a school day are often fraught with tiny rows and acts of minor violence, a biff here, an elbow dig there... Nothing new, nothing new at all. Whose turn is it for the Peter Rabbit plate? Who gets sugar on their Weetabix and who had it last time because if she gets it again it's not fair!? After one such skirmish

I said, 'Come on, let's start again, let's just be friends.' I opened up my arms and said to Millie, 'Come here,' and she said 'No!' 'Why not?' I said, and she said, 'I can't explain...' It occurred to me then how much time has passed in our one year. The growing up that had gone on, inch by inch, the changes. 'The thing is, Mum,' she said, when minutes had gone by. 'The thing is, Mum, I'm shy of you.'

I turned. I asked her 'What? How could you be shy of me?' 'But I am,' she replied, then shook her head; it was like she was trying to shake away her thoughts, trying to get rid of them, frustrated at first that she couldn't express them, but then she said, 'Of all the parts of you that I don't know, I'm shy. The parts of you that were there before I knew you, before – I can't explain it! – I was even born.' She got quite cross. 'I can't explain it!' she cried out. 'But I'm just shy!' And I put down my cloth. I couldn't speak. Didn't even really know then what she meant except that it was true – and now I think I know.

That part of me that now I feel come creeping in, tentatively towards the outskirts of my motherhood, who was there all the time and waiting while the other part of me who is Mum took care... She's coming back. The year is nearly done. I stood behind her, that woman who was me, and together we watched Katherine ascending the stairs – this, two nights ago – watched Katherine's bottom, that rounded confident little shape, a girl in just her knickers going up the stairs and with no need, no thought for a mother... How much time has passed. The woman who was me can feel it, that the woman who is purely and simply Mum is no longer who she used to be. Out shopping the other day I found myself checking in the shadows around my feet, at the pavement behind me, for my daughters who were not with me. I walked up the road, dropped off dry-cleaning, bought some staples and envelopes, visited the vegetable stand where I buy tomatoes, mint, courgettes... The girls were not there. Millie no longer calls for me in the night, Katherine was not on my lap on the bus when I came home... I thought of the Raphael show at the National Gallery I'd visited with her at the beginning of the year and all I could see in those paintings was Katherine, nothing but her in all those babies he'd painted, those paintings of women holding babies, touching babies, besieged by babies... Katherine was all mine then, when I came home with her on the bus… Not now. Instead I stand and watch the bottom in its knickers confidently ascend the stairs.

'Grate work,' wrote Millie on her sister's drawing when they'd been playing schools. Great work indeed. I've never worked so hard as I have since becoming a mother, never wept as much or felt as exhausted, never felt so much joy, either, or pain and pleasure and often both at once, never yelled as much, been as fierce or as tender, never felt such despair and such euphoria… And look at them: all the time while I was on the wheel of feeling, turning, turning, these girls of ours have been quietly making themselves. Growing. Changing. A year passed and time has come, like with any piece of writing I've been working on, to put down my pen… The things are nearly done. And who will I be now? Who will our children be? Nothing seems certain as the one who was me comes back more and more to settle within me, to start in some way again… And how can plans be formed? How to know even how the future might begin? All I do feel certain of is that every year from now on might have this year's same close attention, to the marks, to the lines written down, to the turn of a cheek, the feeling of a hand that still reaches for mine… This year, one year, to mark it all, to stand by in a kind of wonder, actually, that I've been privileged to see this, watch my children grow...

I'm shy of you, Mum...

Katherine, Millie... I'm shy myself.

Notes on the 44 Things

1 *An Introduction*

This is an account of how this book came to be. It was like a little story, looking back on it. I'd been in deep conversations with a great friend who is a painter (she appears in various pieces throughout *44 Things*) about how to make a new kind of art that would accommodate all the demands of motherhood, womanhood. With her enthusiasm and encouragement I'd started thinking about finding a different kind of writing, working in a different kind of way... And then I went to the restaurant with my husband and the girls, and the book followed on from there.

2 *Wahine*

A friend wrote to me about the death of a child, the two-year-old son of a good friend of hers. I didn't know this woman, the boy's mother, but my friend and I talked about her and I made this poem and sent it to her. *Wahine*, as the footnote says, is the Maori word for 'woman' and also the name of a passenger ship that was sunk off Wellington in New

Zealand at the same place the child's ashes were scattered. This is the only piece in *44 Things* where I've changed people's names to maintain privacy.

3 *Notes to Myself*

These lead on from the introduction – asking myself why I believe it to be necessary. I came back to the poetry of Adrienne Rich over these past couple of years, having not read her since I was a teenager. Of course, reading the poems again took the top of my head off. They are vivid and present and real – startlingly accurate representations of the life of a woman who needs to live in her head as well as her heart. When I read Adrienne Rich in the seventies I thought she was making art out of a social situation that no longer existed – that of a woman silenced and disempowered. Now I know otherwise. I refer here to her poem 'Song' from the collection *Diving into the Wreck*.

4 *Small Pieces for the Girls*

Here is a group of small poems, some of them haikus, that I wrote for my two daughters, Millie and Katherine. I love the way the haiku form demands concision, right down to the last syllable – and the five–seven– five syllable per line pattern that I use for all the haikus in *44 Things* seems particularly suited to fragmentary pieces about small children.

5 *Domesticity in Literature: The Art of the Ordinary*

This is the first in a series of essays I found myself writing about the way
the life so many of us have chosen, the life at home, with families and
children, is not fully present or celebrated in literature. I began it as a
piece for the *Guardian* but kept finding I had more and more I wanted to
say. The year finished and there's still more, actually. I'd like to write an
essay on the use of doll's houses in children's books, for example. I'd like
to write about Virginia Woolf and Katherine Mansfield and how they
had no children but their best work is full of families and children.
I'd like to champion the domestic world in books for as long as I live.

6 *Lesley's Tables*

Here I write about a friend who provides a true focus and sense of
warmth in her professional and domestic life. She works at home and is
the mother of three children, who I refer to in the poem, looks after her
husband, and takes care of all her friends by inviting us to the most
wonderful lunches and supper parties. Christine was a dear friend of all
of us, who was dying at the time of writing. I wrote another poem for
her, 'Delphiniums', that appears later in the list of things.

7 *Coming Down off the Hill*

This short story had been rattling around in my head for a while before
I got around to getting it down. I had this image of these three good
friends on their way to a funeral, the way they can't cope with that at all,

and try to find ways of coping. I had an image of them in a car together, driving down a hilly road in the very early morning, the countryside laid out before them in the morning sun. Much later, when it was done, I learned of the death of an old, old friend of mine who lived far away. That was strange. I felt a little as though the story had prepared me for real life. I guess most of my stories do that for me – certainly those that appear in this book.

8 *Annunciation*

I wrote this for a friend who hadn't expected to be pregnant, but was delighted to find out that she was – and then miscarried. The idea for it began when I was walking our dog at Wormwood Scrubs and noticed a little rub of mud or berry stain that wouldn't come off my hand at once. Katherine said to me, 'Why does that mark stay on, Mum?'

9 *Leaves*

A lovely young woman who helped me with Millie when she was small, became, I like to think, a member of our family. While she lived with us she and I would have big discussions about children and parenthood – we had in common the fact that we'd both lost our own mothers when we were young. When she became a mother herself she wrote to me asking how it would ever be possible, in a way, to know what to do, how to be a mother, when we didn't have one ourselves. 'Leaves' was my response to that letter.

10 *Domesticity in Literature: Women at Home in the Novel*
This is the uncut version of the piece I wrote for the *Guardian*. As I
mentioned in the earlier entry, I found I had much to explore on this
subject. A lot of people I didn't know responded to the piece and found
it inspiring – and that delighted me more than I can say. It was as though
the subject of the books became a way of discussing other issues about
motherhood, and being at home with children. It's like the critic Lionel
Trilling says: novels really can provide instruction on how to live. Truly,
they provide an architecture of language and imagination around which
to arrange a life.

11 *Katherine – Still*
Written for my three-year-old daughter, who is a lot like her father,
David. There are references here to various nursery characters she quotes
from TV. 'Clattering softly in' is her way of saying that she's coming
from her bedroom into our bed to sleep with us.

12 *Armature*
The friend I mentioned earlier, who is a painter and sculptor, is the
inspiration for this poem. I really hadn't heard of the word 'armature'
before, which is crazy, I know – apparently it's well known by artists and
non-artists alike – but it gave rise to a great discussion she and I had
that day.

13 *Oh, Veronica!*

Millie's godmother, Irene, who is in the next poem, asked me to
contribute something towards a birthday book she was making for her
sister's sixtieth birthday – and this is what I made her. Veronica and
Cappy live in California but I met them both when I was living with
Irene in New York in the eighties.

14 *How Do I Begin to Say?*

Straight after I made no. 13 I had to make no. 14. How could I not?
I lived with Irene after leaving university while I was working as a waitress
and coat-check in Manhattan. It was an amazing time of calm and
inspiration at a time when my life was quite turbulent. Irene continues
to be a huge part of my life – we talk on the phone and it's like I'm
sitting in her kitchen on Riverside Drive, that no time has passed
between then and now.

15 *Sweeping Up Stars*

This sat in draft form for ages – and yet when I went back to finish it I
didn't know why I had left it behind. It pretty much made itself and took
very little reworking – I could have put it onto the computer from the
start. I love that glitter children use for their artwork, I wish I could
sprinkle it though these pages. I wish every copy of *44 Things* came with
a pack of glitter for everyone to throw around…

16 *The Pass*

I'd written this earlier, I think, in another form, but went back to it in the course of the year to rework it. I'm kind of in love with the themes of it: the silent women in this story, one of whom is in many ways completely unknown — to her own father she is unknown. And yet she's the one telling the story... That idea is powerful, I think.

17 *Poem for Katherine*

Before Katherine started nursery full-time we used to go for a walk each morning at Wormwood Scrubs with our dog, Frank. On certain days the army would be there with their horses and cannons and bugles, practising manoeuvres. It was quite something — a visual spectacle, with marvellous nineteenth-century sound effects. This day, though, they weren't there.

18 *A Woman in a Bedroom*

The same painter friend moved her bed out of her bedroom into the kitchen so she could use her bedroom as a studio. What a thing to do! Inspiring, creative — a wonderful statement of the marriage of creative and domestic life.

19 *'She Knows'*

The title refers to the title of a play within the story, about a mother who has given up her children. While I don't explore the play in the story, I do write about abandonment of different kinds. I note many connecting themes in the stories I wrote over the period of *44 Things*. Abandonment is certainly one.

20 *Pamela's Tree*

A friend had a dreadful cancer diagnosis that put us all into shock — but she herself has managed to rise above the prognosis and inspire us all with her appetite for love and beauty and a lot of fun. This was a birthday card for her.

21 *Roman Sandals*

A photographer friend in New Zealand asked me to write some words to accompany her images of these iconic sandals that we both wore as children. I don't think you can buy them here — a very practical, sturdy kind of sandal. I've ordered two pairs for my daughters to wear this summer.

22 *Words in Translation*

I selected these words from a Maori dictionary and made the translations in a very free, abstract kind of way. Basically the meaning for each word is as follows (but don't take me too literally here): *tatua* = plait; *ngaio* = a kind of tree; *mataatua* = war canoe; *moko* = the tattoo worn on a Maori woman's chin; *tangiwai* = funereal, to do with the dead; *kainga* = house, home.

23 *Domesticity: Stories at Bedtime*

The third essay in a series – I could have made a book of this one subject!
Children's books – the best of them, of course – are utterly riveting and
function on a number of layers that we catch glimpses of in childhood
and that become more fully revealed when we return to them in adult
life. Going back to these books with my daughters now, I see what a huge
influence they have been on me – culturally, imaginatively, morally.
How could I not think that this kind of reading for children is one of
the most important parts of their development?

24 *Ship Song*

Written for my sister about her and her son. Sashimi is the name of her
beloved Burmese cat who died some time ago – but who still slips around
the place, like dear pets who've died do, in the corner of our vision. Her
marriage was ending at the time of writing, hence the image of her son,
Jamie, as a ship out there on his own. We could use this image for all our
children, I think. Remember the title of that Robert Louis Stevenson
poem, 'Where Go the Boats?'

25 *Now I can see how it was, I think*

These two sisters got a hold of me and I write about them here, as
children, and then later in 'Sisters' when they're grown up. I'm pretty
sure they're the same two. I think they've been around for a while.

I love writing from a child's perspective, I love the freedom it gives —
of expression, of vision, the way things are seen in hectic, vivid colours.

26 *Not to Go Up*
One of those overpowering moments when we feel the lurch of time —
suddenly our children have gone from one phase of their lives into the
next. I'd been downstairs working away at something in the kitchen and
Millie had kept calling and calling for me to go up — but I kept resisting
it… Thinking it was good for her, good for me to do so. I don't know.
What good those kinds of thoughts? I went up into the dark of her room
and there she was crying and crying and I took her into my arms.

27 *Tender*
This is a memory of being pregnant with Katherine. I would be exhausted
in the early afternoon and would fall into bed with Millie, who still had
a bottle of milk then, and we would both of us drift, pretty quickly
actually, into a dreamy, afternoon sleep.

28 *Invitation to a Dance*
Another of those moments when you realize life and time are on the
move. You don't see the change coming but look back and see how
different things are now, and how, though it may feel a little sad to be
moving on, you want to accommodate that difference, welcome it,
enjoy it.

29 *Letter to my Sister*

Written long after the time in the hospital the letter refers to, when my sister was diagnosed with breast cancer. We were in her garden and had this moment of... seeing. Even then it took me a while to write to her about it. I would like to show it to the three children some day — maybe they can help me explain it.

30 *The Dream Bird*

This was one of those clear, vivid dreams that stay in your head like a film or picture. I had no doubt when I woke that the bird was me.

31 *Book Review: Rules of Detachment*

This was a review of a book I enjoyed enormously for its engaging literary take on — more than anything else, I think — domestic life. I'm not sure that was entirely the writer's intention — there were things going on in the actual writing that showed he was probably more preoccupied with style and surface — but I couldn't help but settle into all the detail about home-making and how the furniture was arranged and what they were going to eat that evening. The writer was terrific on all that, the sheer cosiness of home-life. My husband's been reading *Little House on the Prairie* to the girls and it has a similar appeal, I think.

32 *At the Acupuncturist*

Gerad, the acupuncturist who appears here, could not believe Katherine when he met her. We arrived at his practice on Harley Street and Gerad asked Katherine if she wanted me to go in at the beginning of the appointment or stay in the waiting room. She said she wanted to go up with Gerad on her own. So I went up later. Gerad opened the door, and said, just like that, 'Your daughter's a trip!' He's wonderful, by the way. He did sort out the things Katherine wanted him to.

33 *Delphiniums*

Christine, who I've mentioned before, an artist, a mother, friend, a groovy, inspiring woman with an amazing turn of phrase... did die. It happened so fast it was hard to believe — still is. As I said earlier, in 'Lesley's Tables', there's a space on the table for her things. Part of Lesley, I know, wants to keep a seat for her.

34 *Sisters*

This is a short story I made a few years ago — but it wasn't finished properly then and was in a very different form. I came back to it and couldn't believe how much it had been a part of my unconscious over the intervening years. Surely the sisters are related to those in 'Now I can see how it was, I think' — certainly, there's more to write about them yet.

35 *The Sheep and the Lambs*

I wrote this up in the Highlands where I was teaching a creative-writing course. It was a beautiful September – but then September is always beautiful in Scotland.

36 *Drawings – Fragment*

This is taken from a much longer story that I wrote many years ago and that was never really finished but continues to surface, aspects of it, in many of my short stories. I went back to it during this past year and realized this – so wanted to include a small part of it here. Sometime I'll sit down and write fully about that boy in New York who's all grown up now but carries memories of horses with him, and can't stop drawing them, but in outlines he can barely see.

37 *Katherine and the Mouse*

There's a crack by our front door where the mouse's family live. This morning Katherine said, 'Look!' in the same way as she says it in the poem and at first I thought she'd seen the little mouse again – but this time she was pointing at a bee.

38 *Boys and Bikinis*

Written for *Vogue* magazine as a way of also telling people about my new novel, *The Boy and the Sea*. I've talked a lot about bikinis since – and women have a lot to say on the subject. I'm going to be counting the number of mothers I see in bikinis this summer. I'll be wanting to tell all of them how great they look.

39 *Small Pieces for the Girls*

More of these little haiku poems — the haiku seems to suit that ping! of emotion one has when looking at one's children. Often I scribbled them on a scrap of paper, at the bottom of one of my endless lists. Or I'd just wildly try to memorize it at the time of its happening — that could cause a bit of craziness, a chorus of ascending 'Mum!'s.

40 *Car*

I used to write short stories like this all the time. When I was younger, when I wanted a form for a subject that felt utterly contemporary. I loved writing that way — and then I kind of slowly stopped doing it. The stories got longer, and longer... And then, this story! 'Sudden Fiction' it used to be called in the eighties. What a wonderful genre that is.

41 *Katherine in a Red Towel*

What is it about children and towels at bath-time? It's like kittens on chocolate boxes, puppies under the tree at Christmas... Ridiculous, but what can you do?

42 *The Sea in Literature*

An essay I'd wanted to write as I'd been thinking about the subject in relation to the novel I mentioned earlier. When writing that book I'd realized that the sea, a deeply female and maternal presence in the story, would have to be a character, actually. That she would have to speak. I wanted to describe the context for this kind of thinking in a more objective way.

43 Ceol Mor

Another thing to include in this book might be a recording of my father playing this lament — we could put it in, along with the packet of glitter. Lament for all our children, how they leave us, how they must leave. Since writing the haiku, Milllie and Katherine do still come into our bed — but it's by no means the routine thing it used to be. Bit by bit, those routines are changing. Of course, they must.

44 A Farewell

Here we are at the end of my year. The sound of the lament is still there, drifting in a pale blue Highland sky — but something else is in the air too: change. Who will David and I be, I wonder, in the times that are to come? Who will I be? What will the next year bring? And the years after? How many 'things' can we accumulate, patch together like a quilt and comfort ourselves with when we are lonely or troubled or cold? I hope hundreds. Forty-four times forty-four times forty-four... Every day, every week, every month... To gather up and celebrate, keep somehow safe, as though forever.

Acknowledgements

I've never included acknowledgements in my books before, in the novels, short stories... To have done so would have seemed too intrusive somehow, as though I would have been imposing too much of me and my life upon a fictional landscape, disturbing the imaginative quiet of that landscape with the sound of my own voice.

This book is different. It's been made in a different way, for a different purpose. Whereas the other work would have come together no matter what, would have been written through and completed, *44 Things*, quite simply, would not be a book at all without the enthusiasm and encouragement of the following people. So, with my arms wide open, I want to say Thank you!...

Firstly to Whitney McVeigh who saw the very first scrap of a thing and said, 'Keep this, Kirsty, build on this...' Nothing would have followed the way it did without her friendship and support.

Then to my husband, David Graham, who sat with me in the restaurant that night and said, 'I think there could be a book in this...' Without his thoughts *44 Things* would have stayed in my folder and never been gathered together in the way it has been. Then to John Carey, thank you, and David Miller and Dominique Bourgois, all parents who saw in the little things they read parts of their own lives, and piled in from the start with enthusiasm. And thank you to Toby Mundy, publisher and new-born father who let out a loud 'Yes!' when he heard about the project and lent his intelligence and support to it from that minute on. Thank you, too, Daniel Scott, also at Atlantic, who came in at the start with energy and vision, and Valerie Duff, my sensitive and insightful editor there, a mother who reads me back this work and makes me hear it again through her own voice. Thank you to my own sister, Merran Gunn, and my dear friend Lesley Bryce, both of whom patiently read and listen to the things I write and always give advice that is clever and wise and true, thank you. And to all the people in *44 Things* who are my friends and family, and whose friendship and intimacy set off the spark of a thing, who made it begin: thank you, thank you, thank you.